S0-BAY-547

Minding Your Body

Minding Your Body

Norman D. Ford

AUTUMN PRESS

Published by Autumn Press, Inc.
with editorial offices at
1318 Beacon Street
Brookline, Massachusetts 02146

Copyright © 1981 by Norman D. Ford. All rights reserved.
ISBN: 0-914398-30-X
Library of Congress Catalog Number: 81-66774
Printed in the United States of America
Typeset at dnh, Cambridge, Massachusetts

Book design and typography by Michael Fender
Cover design © 1981 by Robert Silverman

Contents

Inner Healing
Techniques

Acknowledgments

MUCH OF THIS BOOK is based on studies by eminent authorities in scientific and medical disciplines. Almost all these studies support the validity and effectiveness of the holistic approach to health care and of the various inner healing techniques. I have also drawn extensively on case histories from natural healing clinics, pain clinics, and rehabilitation centers where holistic philosophy is practiced. In most cases, the patients' names have been changed to protect their identity.

So many direct and indirect sources were consulted in researching this book that it is impractical to acknowledge every one. However, I would like to acknowledge my debt to the works of Emil Coué; Elmer and Alyce Green; O. Carl Simonton, M.D., and Stephanie Matthews-Simonton; Kenneth R. Pelletier; Robert A. Anderson, M.D.; Swami Rama; Swami Satchidananda; Ken Keyes, Jr.; and the hundreds of other contemporary holistic health pioneers who collectively have taught us that the higher our level of consciousness, the higher our level of health.

Minding Your Body

1. Thoughts That Heal

FOR DECADES, psychologists have known that we use only 10 percent of our mental capacity.

What is not as well known is that during the past decade or so, hundreds of people—scientific teams and researchers, yoga swamis and individual thinkers—have plumbed at least some of the mysteries of that other, unknown 90 percent of the human mind.

What they have found is that the inner world of the mind has amazing powers to eliminate emotional stress, to end pain and suffering, to heal disease, and to maintain a level of wellness far higher than that experienced by most Americans in this high-pressure age.

Although ancient peoples knew and used this inner healing power, it was not until the 1950s that its existence was confirmed by medical science. Using sensitive electronic devices called biofeedback machines, researchers discovered that a person could achieve significant control over the involuntary function of the heart, nervous system, arteries, endocrine glands, and blood pressure.

Patients were hooked up to the machines, which measured the degree of muscle relaxation, skin temperature, and brain-wave frequency. As each of these functions speeded up or slowed down, the machines would indicate the change by emitting audible beeps. With constant feedback from the machines to monitor their progress, patients would quickly learn to speed up or slow down their heart rate, to raise or lower their blood pressure, to relax their entire nervous system, or even to rebalance the chemistry of their endocrine/hormone system. By thinking certain thoughts, patients could slow their brain wave, warm their hands, or enter a state of deep relaxation.

Biofeedback techniques were developed under laboratory conditions in medical centers such as the Menninger Foundation and the Mayo Clinic, and today biofeedback is widely accepted in the treatment of hypertension (high blood pressure), headaches, pain, and a variety of conditions attributed to anxiety, tension, and emotional stress. Biofeedback taught us that mind and body are inextricably linked. Simply by sliding a certain thought into our mind, we can cause a major involuntary change in the body, often within a few seconds. A thought about something as calm and serene as a beautiful garden can cause our nervous system to relax, our arteries to dilate, our blood pressure to drop, and our heart rate and respiratory rate to slow.

You may never have thought much about it before, but there is ample evidence that the body involuntarily responds almost immediately to whatever thought crosses your mind. Think a pleasant thought and you smile. Think a melancholy thought and you immediately feel sad. Think an angry thought and you frown. Think an embarrassing thought and you blush. Think a fearful thought and you tense. Think about an attractive member of the opposite sex and you become excited.

What is so impressive is the dramatic swiftness with which our thoughts are translated into major physiological changes that we could not possibly duplicate by voluntary means. Within a split second after we see a danger, say a car or truck coming toward us, a reflex action prompts us to dash from its path. A second later, a thought of danger pops into our mind, setting off a profound feeling of fear. This fear triggers the hypothalamus, the gland located in the brain that controls many involuntary body functions, to switch on the fight-or-flight emergency state, a primitive survival response. Glands throughout the body squirt adrenaline and other hormones into the bloodstream, our heart rate speeds up, blood pressure rises, and energy is released to power and tense our muscles to either attack or flee. Within the space of a few seconds, a thought of danger can transform our entire physical and mental state.

Biofeedback research has also confirmed that not only does every change in thought cause a corresponding change in body function, but also that every change in body function is accompanied by a corresponding change in our feelings and thoughts.

An example of this two-way interaction is the relationship between anxiety or fear and muscular tension. Tension is created when anxiety or fear triggers the fight-or-flight response and energy floods into our muscles to tense them for action. If no physical action occurs, we simply remain tense. But tension cannot exist when the mind is calm. If we replace thoughts of fear with thoughts of calm and peace, our tension soon subsides. Conversely, by exercising and burning up the energy that is causing our muscles to tense, we can squeeze fear and anxiety out of our mind.

14

Healing with the Mind

Many exercises and techniques have been developed that use this intimate relationship between our mental processes and our physical state to focus our thoughts on our inner healing power. My purpose in this book is to describe how you can use these inner healing techniques to improve your own health and to help reverse painful and crippling disease.

The fact that these techniques are freely available to anyone has been kept fairly well hidden. Biofeedback, for example, is available at most hospitals and medical centers and therefore has become a fairly expensive form of therapy. Yet many of the benefits of biofeedback can be achieved by almost anyone through several easily learned inner healing techniques that require neither paid instruction nor elaborate monitoring equipment.

The techniques described in this book take you step by step from the elementary level of attaining deep relaxation to gaining voluntary control over your arteries, nervous system, and inner organs. There are techniques for modifying your belief system to eliminate health-destroying emotional stress and there are exercises you can use to guide your imagination to help your body overcome disease and attain a permanent state of high-level wellness.

The techniques described in this book are currently being used by several hundred pain clinics across the United States to teach people to phase out the pain of chronic diseases, including arthritis, gout, and lower back dysfunctions. By learning to relax the vasoconstrictor muscles in their hands and feet—muscles that can constrict the arteries and cut off blood flow—thousands of people have been able to lower their high blood pressure to safe levels without drugs or to put a permanent stop to a lifetime of crippling migraine headaches. Other thousands of men and women have been able to eliminate destructive emotional stress from their lives and replace it with health-building peace, serenity, and calm.

The technique of guided imagery—guiding the mind to imagine vivid pictures of desired health goals—has helped thousands of people recover from diseases such as obesity, diabetes, heart disease, and even medically diagnosed cancer.

Much of the pioneer work in developing guided imagery was carried out on terminal cancer patients by Dr. O. Carl Simonton and Stephanie Matthews-Simonton, medical director and counseling director, respectively, of the Cancer Counseling and Research Center in Fort Worth, Texas. Between 1974 and 1978 the Simontons taught guided imagery to 159 patients diagnosed as having medically incurable cancer. At the end of the four-year period, sixty-three of the patients were still alive and these had an average survival time of 24.4 months. Fourteen of the survivors showed a complete remission of cancer. In twelve the cancer was regressing. And in seventeen the disease was stable. Even those who died had an average survival time of 20.3 months.

These statistics contrast rather dramatically with those for terminal cancer patients who did not practice guided imagery. Over the same four-year period, the life expectancy of terminal cancer patients in the general population averaged only twelve months while only one in one hundred achieved a natural remission and recovered from cancer completely.

The Simontons are careful not to claim that they have found a universal cure for cancer. The success of their treatment depends to a great extent on the patient's own belief that he or she will recover from the disease and on how well he or she cooperates with the imagery sessions.

When the Simontons examined their patients' personality profiles, they found an almost direct relationship between those who believed they would recover and those who actually did recover. Patients who achieved either a complete remission or a regression ranked among those with the strongest beliefs in their ability to overcome the disease. Each had a strongly positive attitude toward recovery and each cooperated enthusiastically in practicing the imagery therapy.

Virtually all those who died had felt themselves helpless victims of their disease and had failed to practice their imagery regularly. If we statistically disregard the patients who failed to cooperate with the therapy, the Simontons' recovery rate is revealed as phenomenally successful.

On the basis of the Simontons' results, it appears that patients who sincerely believe they can overcome cancer and who faithfully practice the guided imagery stand at least one chance in three of achieving a remission or regression from cancer medically classified as incurable. The Simontons' results have provided irrefutable confirmation that *as we think and imagine and feel and believe, so we become.*

Harnessing Your Extra Imagination

Elaine Rogers is typical of the kind of patient treated by the Simontons. In 1975 Elaine was hospitalized with a tumor in her spine. Doctors operated and confirmed that the tumor was malignant, but they were unable to remove it. At age thirty-five, Elaine was discharged as incurable and sent home to die.

Instead of giving up, Elaine read all she could about her disease. She learned that cancer is usually triggered by emotional stress and that the typical cancer patient often has deeply suppressed anger and has difficulty expressing feelings. For the next few months Elaine lived in a quiet, stress-free setting with an abundance of love and support from her husband and children. Under these favorable conditions her cancer seemed to stabilize.

At this point she learned about the work of the Simontons and she enrolled at the Cancer Counseling and Research Center in Fort Worth.

Simonton taught her how to bring her body to a level of relaxation and how to picture her tumor in her mind's eye on an imaginary movie screen. Three times a day for fifteen minutes Elaine created a vivid picture of her tumor becoming smaller and smaller. She visualized swarms of her body's white "soldier" cells ferociously tearing the cancer cells apart with their jagged teeth. Toward the end of each session she pictured her white cells flushing the mutilated remains of the cancer cells out of her body in her urine.

Whenever she experienced a doubt about the success of her treatment, Elaine would use a thought-stopping technique. She would arrest the thought process immediately by pinching her wrist. Then she would slide the negative thought to one side and replace it with an image of herself in perfect health jogging along a Florida beach.

As she practiced her daily imagery, Elaine realized that she was regaining control of her life and that she was taking an active role in her own recovery.

Whenever she felt pain she slipped the thought into her mind that the pain was caused as her white cells destroyed the tumor. Soon she began to welcome the very pains she had earlier dreaded.

But as the weeks went by, the pains gradually subsided and Elaine began to feel better. As the time approached for her medical examination, Elaine visualized herself being examined for cancer in the doctor's office. In her imagination she pictured the doctor unable to find a trace of cancer.

Exactly eleven months after she had first been diagnosed as having cancer, Elaine stood in the same doctor's office awaiting the results of her diagnostic tests.

"We can find no trace of cancer," the doctor told her. "My original diagnosis must have been in error. No one could possibly recover from cancer of the spine without surgical removal followed by chemotherapy and radiation treatment."

"No, your diagnosis was correct," Elaine replied. "I reversed the cancer myself using a visualization technique . . ."

But the doctor had already left the room. He refused to listen to her explanation.

As this was written, Elaine Rogers was still living a healthy, active life with no indication of ever having had a spinal malignancy.

We Are What We Think

Guided imagery and other inner healing techniques have taught us that just as we are what we eat, so we are what we think. A dozen separate studies have confirmed that we invariably become what we think, feel, imagine, and believe we are.

We can think ourselves sick. Or we can think ourselves well.

The function of the human mind has turned out to be almost identical to that of a complex electronic computer, complete with its own biological memory banks, feedback circuits, interpretive ability, and videotapes with instant playback.

In principle, the various inner healing techniques are simply methods for programming our own mind-computer. For instance, we can reprogram our minds so that a stressful event that usually turns on destructive emotions such as envy, anger, or fear is interpreted instead as a pleasant, calming experience.

Jones and Smith are both laid off from their jobs. Jones sees unemployment as a financial disaster that threatens the loss of everything he owns. But Smith views her unemployment as a blessed release from a boring, monotonous job and as an opportunity to seek more interesting, better-paid work.

Both people experience the same event through their mind-computers. But obviously Jones's programming, which is causing him to view unemployment as a threat, is exactly the opposite of the programming that makes Smith view unemployment as a welcome opportunity.

Our mind-computer is programmed by the beliefs and experiences we have accumulated over a lifetime. Most of our beliefs and values were acquired years ago; they may date back ten, twenty, even fifty or more years. All too often they create a negative attitude like Jones's, which could be entirely inappropriate for the times in which we are living.

But Jones doesn't have to let his life continue to be run by outdated programming. He can update his belief system so that his mind-computer views the world in a positive and optimistic way.

A few years ago such a concept would have been considered unthinkable. But revolutionary systems like est and Rational Emotive Therapy have proved that we can program our mind to react positively to a stressful event after only a few days of practice. We can choose to view mandatory retirement as a sign that we are unneeded and unemployable. Or we can choose to view it as an opportunity to make a mid-life change to a career we find interesting and worthwhile.

Whether our mind-computer is programmed by a positive or a negative belief system is a crucial factor in determining our health. Stress occurs when we are faced with a life change to which we must adjust, such as marriage, a new baby, divorce, or death. For millions of Americans, mandatory retirement is a change that heralds a threat of reduced income, lower living standards, and interminable boredom. Even though retirement may be years away, the fact that our mind-computer interprets future retirement as a threat is sufficient to invoke doubtful thoughts and feelings of fear, anxiety, and worry. Such negative feelings send the hypothalamus into an alarm state and switch on the fight-or-flight response.

The simple act of thinking about retirement ten years from now turns on the same bodywide emergency state we would experience if suddenly faced by a hungry tiger. It is true that the impact is not as intense. Nonetheless, the thought of a lifestyle change like retirement sets up a low-level emergency state that continues to smolder for as long as we keep having negative thoughts about retirement.

Studies show that people who suffer from such crippling and killing diseases as ulcers, cancer, heart disease, diabetes, arthritis, gout, and kidney disease live much of their lives in this stressful emergency state.

Personality profiles made of tens of thousands of people suffering from these chronic diseases show that they invariably have deeply repressed feelings of hostility and anger. Heart disease sufferers are often human dynamos who drive themselves under constant pressure in an effort to create security by building a fortress of money and possessions. People who get ulcers or cancer frequently have difficulty expressing their feelings. They repress negative emotions such as worry, fear, anxiety, hatred, envy, and anger while outwardly they make themselves appear to be likable, calm, and agreeable. The stress of this inner conflict suppresses their body's defense system, which then becomes unable to fight off disease. Cancer patients often display feelings of helplessness and passivity, and many have personality profiles that are almost identical to those of people who attempt or commit suicide.

All of these negative emotions—anger, hatred, envy, fear, worry, and anxiety—occur when our mind-computer interprets an external event as threatening or unfriendly. Whether our mind-computer interprets a stimulus as threatening depends on our programming, that is, on whether we have a positive or negative belief system. People with negative belief systems—inappropriate, self-centered beliefs based on primitive instincts—tend to interpret as stressful anything that may change their lifestyle. These are the same people who become sick or die from heart disease, cancer, diabetes, obesity, ulcers, arthritis, and all the other melancholy litany of degenerative diseases.

People with positive belief systems built on love, trust, generosity, and other civilized values accept life as it is and see changes as learning experiences or as interesting adventures. They tend to enjoy persistent good health and seldom suffer from chronic disease. These positive beliefs are similar to those found in every religion. Studies have shown that religious people live longer, have lower blood pressure, and enjoy a more active and satisfying sex life than do most nonreligious people. A recent study of 35,460 Seventh-Day Adventists in California showed, for instance, that the average church member lived seven years longer than the average Californian, and 70 percent fewer Adventists died of cancer and 60 percent fewer died of heart disease.

New Mind, New Body

All of this goes to show that what we feed our minds is at least as important to our health as what we feed our bodies. Later in this book you will read how you can reprogram your mind-computer so that you create a healthy, relaxed personality instead of a self-destructive, disease-prone one.

To do so, it isn't necessary to give up your possessions or to make radical changes in the way you live. All you need do is reprogram your attitudes so that your mind-computer stops interpreting the world as an unfriendly, threatening place.

Recent discoveries have demonstrated that mind and body are a single, integrated organism. But ever since Descartes separated the concepts of body and mind in the seventeenth century the progress of medical science has been hindered by a philosophy that treats our mental and physical functions as entirely separate entities. Until recently, patients with emotional problems spent months or even years undergoing cumbersome psychiatric treatments that considered only the mind instead of the whole person and that often accomplished very little. The same dualistic philosophy has turned doctors into mechanics, training them to treat the body like an automobile engine instead of as a living organism run by its own mind-computer. Although it is generally accepted now that our most common diseases are triggered by stress and are caused by our own incorrect habits of living and eating, drugs and surgery are still regarded as the only orthodox ways to treat most diseases.

Topping the list of today's most crippling and lethal diseases are degenerative diseases: stroke, heart attack, hypertension, atherosclerosis, cancer, diabetes, obesity, arthritis, gout, kidney disease, ulcerative colitis, and osteoporosis (bone loss). All are slow-onset diseases, that is, they take years or decades to materialize. Instead of being caused by "germs," these modern-day killers are caused by a combination of emotional stress and our soft, easy, mechanized lifestyle, which discourages exercise, encourages an artificial, salty, high-fat diet, and makes toxic drugs, including caffeine and nicotine, an acceptable part of everyday living.

Millions of tranquilizers are swallowed every day by Americans who are unable to cope with their emotional stress. Millions of people with high blood pressure or diabetes have been casually placed on maintenance

20

drugs for life despite the medically proven fact that both diseases respond readily to exercise and a low-fat diet.

No one would deny the benefits of modern medical care for emergencies of any kind—burns, injuries, trauma, shock—as well as for a wide range of infectious and other life-threatening diseases. Through its success in handling these short-term crises, medical science has come to practice what is best described as crisis medicine.

Many physicians themselves admit that crisis medicine can do little to cure slow-onset diseases that are triggered by stress and everyday living habits. The fact is that neither drugs nor surgery have so far produced a single bona fide cure for any degenerative disease, including cancer and heart disease. Cutting out a malignant tumor and exposing the patient to extremely toxic chemotherapy and radiation can hardly be considered a genuine cure for cancer. Nor can stripping a vein from a leg and using it to form new arteries to bypass a patient's own coronary arteries that are blocked with cholesterol.

In neither case has the *cause* of the disease been treated. All too often cancer reappears soon after a tumor has been removed. And unless a person makes a total lifestyle change, new coronary bypass arteries can become blocked within a year if the patient continues to eat a diet high in fats.

Other drawbacks to medical treatment, such as the awesome side effects of prescription drugs or the possibility of an expensive unnecessary operation, are too well known to warrant discussion here.

It is not my intention to discourage anyone from undergoing necessary medical treatment. In fact, I would strongly urge any reader with any kind of persistent pain or other sign of possible illness or injury to see a doctor immediately for a professional diagnosis. You should also check with your doctor before practicing inner healing techniques if you have any serious psychological problem. Likewise, if you are on maintenance drugs or have any life-threatening condition, you should check with your doctor before making any changes. The inner healing techniques in this book are not intended as an alternative to necessary medical treatment by a competent physician. Rather, they can be used to reinforce and boost the benefits of orthodox medical care.

Nonetheless, as the shortcomings of drugs and surgery have become more apparent, millions of laypeople, as well as many conscientious doctors, have become increasingly disenchanted with the inability of orthodox medicine to treat degenerative disease. Along with the growing knowledge about the role of our own mind-computers in maintaining health has emerged an entirely new philosophy of health care based on treating the whole person as a single living entity.

The Holistic Approach to a Healthy Lifestyle

Holistic health care treats the whole person: physically, mentally, emotionally, and spiritually. It recognizes that allopathy (medical treatment) has no monopoly on healing and that gentle, natural therapies like acupuncture, fasting, nutrition, or yoga are frequently as successful in restoring health as are powerful drugs or surgery. All of the recently developed inner healing techniques described in this book are an integral part of a holistic approach.

A vital difference between allopathy and holistic philosophy is the patient's own attitude. Most patients go to see a doctor with a passive, helpless feeling that they have no control over their own disease. They believe that a disease is something that just happened to them and cannot possibly be due to their own self-defeating habits of thinking, living, and eating. They have spent many years shifting the responsibility for their health onto their physician and they are conditioned to expect that somehow they can be made well by a drug, an injection, or an operation that is worked on them while they take no part whatsoever in their own recovery.

In contrast, people who elect holistic treatment are required to accept full responsibility for the onset of their disease and to take an active role in their own recovery. That does not mean they are to blame for their disease. People who get emphysema from smoking cigarettes (usually as a release from emotional stress) are not blamed for what they have done. But they are expected to recognize those aspects of their lives that lead to stress and, in turn, to smoking. This enables them to take an active part in their recovery by working at eliminating those behaviors as the real cause of their disease.

While medical science admits it has no cure for most degenerative diseases and confines itself to alleviating symptoms, the aim of holistic health care is to treat and remove the cause of disease. When the cause of disease is removed, the body's own recuperative powers are usually able to overcome the disease and restore health. Inner healing techniques can be of inestimable value by helping to eliminate stress and by reinforcing the body's defenses as they mobilize to annihilate disease.

Genuine disease reversal cannot occur while a patient continues to hold a passive and helpless attitude. Studies have shown that terminal cancer patients who become angry and rage at their disease survive almost twice as long as do patients who passively accept their illness and believe they have no control over it.

A patient who chooses to passively continue taking a drug instead of actively changing his or her own life-threatening beliefs and lifestyle is considered by the majority of holistic practitioners to be deliberately avoiding responsibility for his or her own health and well-being. The act of taking a pill is effortless, but genuine recovery from a chronic disease calls for effort and cooperation by the patient. Frequently a holistic approach offers the only hope of permanent recovery from many chronic diseases, including arthritis, heart disease, diabetes, and ulcerative colitis.

The holistic approach does not exclude medical care. It simply points out that true health can be achieved only when the whole person is functioning smoothly—physically, mentally, emotionally, and spiritually. The holistic view is that most illness is caused by the stress of life events, not by a virus or by aging or degeneration.

Holistic Wellness Defined

While a physician may pronounce a person in "good health" if the person shows no sign of disease during a routine checkup and diagnostic tests, the holistic definition of health is quite different. Genuine health is so inadequately portrayed by the word *health* that holistic practitioners prefer the term *wellness*.

Rene Dubos, an eminent microbiologist at Rockefeller University, has written that "human health is as much dependent on environmental and emotional factors as on measurements of blood pressure or temperature. Good health implies an individual's success in functioning within his particular set of values. Good health is primarily a measure of each person's ability to do what he wants to do and become. The concept of health as a creative, adaptive process seems at odds with the dominant creed of modern scientific medicine."

Thus a holistic practitioner is likely to ask you how you feel about yourself and your life rather than where your pain is located. If you suffer from chronic pain, the holistic approach suggests that you consider what your pain is telling you about yourself, about the way you feel toward your life, your goals, your job, your environment, and the people with whom you interact.

Our living habits are molded by the way we feel about the world around us; and how we feel is controlled by the way we have programmed our mind-computer to interpret life's events. A holistic practitioner does not believe that drugs can cure a disease brought on by the way we feel about ourselves and the world around us. A drug may stop the pain of arthritis for a while. But as soon as we stop taking the drug, the pain returns with renewed intensity. Many expensive drugs merely serve to alleviate symptoms instead of seeking out and eliminating the causes of disease. Emotional stress and destructive living habits—the causes of most degenerative diseases—are totally beyond the reach of the effects of any drug.

Holistic philosophy places the power to turn our health around in our own hands. Through inner healing techniques we can unlock our vast untapped inner resources to gain access to our inner self and our emotional states. Just as a physician intervenes in our physical health, so we ourselves can use psychological intervention to reprogram a belief system that is making us sick: to switch from a negative to a positive state of mind, to phase out self-destructive habits, and to assume complete control over our health and our lives.

Inner healing therapy works on the emotional level, but to achieve a truly holistic approach we should not neglect the physical aspects of health, such as exercise and diet. The Simontons, for example, report that terminal cancer patients who exercise regularly in conjunction with their guided imagery therapy recover significantly faster than patients who do not exercise.

The New Health

Out of the experiences of holistic health practitioners has come the holistic equation for health:

Diet + Exercise + Positive Thinking = High-Level Wellness.

Although holistic principles have gained wide acceptance, holistic health care remains primarily a do-it-yourself thing. It embraces all forms of health care and therapy, including allopathy, chiropractic, naturopathy, homeopathy, natural hygiene, nutrition, hydrotherapy, massage, exercise, yoga, and poetry and dance therapy. Nothing with demonstrable therapeutic value is ignored and no single modality is considered more important or superior to another.

True holistic treatment centers are comparatively rare. Pain clinics and cardiac rehabilitation centers use the holistic approach, but only a handful of total lifestyle systems, such as hatha yoga, integral yoga, and the Seventh-Day Adventist church, actually offer completely holistic health care on the physical, mental, emotional, and spiritual levels simultaneously.

Further, the holistic movement itself has diverged along two quite different paths, the physical and the psychological. The adherents to one path often know little about the work of adherents to the other.

The physical path is that taken by most professional healers: the biofeedback psychologists, physicians, chiropractors, naturopaths, natural hygiene practitioners, massage practitioners, and nutritionists. Their emphasis is on treating physical symptoms of disease by changing patients' lifestyle habits. Fasting, exercise, and diet are typical therapies and results are often dramatic. But because these physical healers do not treat the mental, spiritual, and emotional systems, the destructive beliefs that trigger stress are still present, and patients often stray back to their former living habits and disease reappears.

Inner healing techniques with physical effects, such as progressive relaxation, guided imagery, and warming the hands and feet, are of immense value in helping patients gain voluntary control over their inner organs and in motivating the physical body to recover from chronic disease.

The psychological path is that taken by religious organizations such as the Unity church and the Seventh-Day Adventist church, by sufis and yoga swamis, and by such philosophies as est, Living Love, and Rational Emotive Therapy. The emphasis of these philosophies is on reprogramming our belief system so that our mind-computer interprets stress as harmless. Hatha yoga, integral yoga, and the Seventh-Day Adventist church endorse nutritional principles and exercise, and others concentrate on psychological techniques alone.

The patient who consults the average chiropractor or naturopath in the hope of finding a holistic practitioner is likely to discover that the healer knows little of biofeedback or hand-warming therapies, to say nothing of such subjective techniques as reprogramming our belief system or taking responsibility for our disease. It is largely left to patients themselves to select the modalities that seem to best fill the holistic equation in their lives. This is not a bad idea, for a person is likely to intuitively select those therapies that suit him or her best.

This book can be used as a guide along both the physical and psychological paths in your efforts to seek treatment that is holistic. The only preparation you need to begin experiencing these new methods of health care is a basic familiarity with human physiology and the fundamentals of diet and exercise. You should already know enough about the basics of nutrition to realize that most rapid weight-loss diets are unholistic, stressful, and ineffective. And you should be content to begin a progressive exercise program with nothing more strenuous than a brisk daily walk.

The body responds to vivid mental pictures of healing that are repeatedly produced in the imagination. For greatest effect, the pictures must show specific body processes. The body itself will then respond by carrying out the processes the mind has suggested. To picture these healing body processes you need at least an elementary idea of the physiological effects of some of the more common diseases. The following chapter will supply some of that fundamental physiology by tracing the progress of stressful life events into life-threatening diseases.

2. *Thoughts That Kill*

CHARLOTTE LAGRANGE of Lake Worth, Florida, had suffered for years from agonizing rheumatoid arthritis pains in her fingers and hands. Doctors could do nothing to help. Only constant medication could deaden the pain. Finally, Charlotte's hands became so stiff she could no longer do simple household chores.

At the local Wickershaw Pain Clinic, therapists taught Charlotte that pain could not be felt until a thought of pain had first entered the mind.

"A thought of pain always precedes a feeling of pain," the therapist told Charlotte. "What does your pain feel like?"

"Like a red-hot fire," Charlotte replied.

"What would extinguish the fire?"

"A bucket of ice water," Charlotte said.

The therapist showed Charlotte a simple technique that took her swiftly into a state of deep relaxation. Then he taught her to visualize her pain as a red-hot fire. In her imagination she then plunged both hands into buckets of ice water.

Charlotte was instructed to visualize the same scene repeatedly for fifteen minutes three times each day.

By the fourteenth day Charlotte was able to stop taking pain medication. At this point the therapist instructed her to spend the final five minutes of each session visualizing her hands as completely healed and well. Only twenty-eight days after she first began using guided imagery, Charlotte's hands and fingers were completely flexible and free of pain. Gradually she cut back the imagery sessions to only three per week. On the rare occasions when a flare-up does occur, she can quell it in a few hours by imagining that the pain has disappeared.

Charlotte's success hinged on the facts that a thought always precedes a feeling and that we can think only one thought at a time.

The fact that her pain felt like a fire gave the therapist a clue to the nature of the thought that preceded her pain. He then instructed Charlotte to displace this thought with a diametrically opposite thought. The thought of ice water evoked a feeling that had the opposite effect: it deadened Charlotte's pain. Gradually, session by session, Charlotte's body chemistry began to conform with the images she had created in her mind.

We can only speculate about the cause of Charlotte's arthritis. But a growing majority of medical researchers today believe that at least 80 percent of all human ailments are the result of emotional stress.

Their creed? *What the mind can cause, the mind can reverse and heal.*

How Our Mind-Computer Processes Thought

A thought is a mental image. We hold this thought in our mind like an index card while we see it projected on our mental movie screen. One thought flows smoothly into another, creating a movie of the mind complete with inner sound—mind-chatter that converses with our awareness.

Most thoughts are involuntary responses to the input of stimuli into our mind-computer. Unless deliberately meditating, which makes the mind blank, we are constantly, but involuntarily, choosing random thoughts, each prompted by the previous thought or by input data reaching the mind.

We can also choose voluntary thoughts, which take precedence over involuntary thoughts. The technique of guided imagery is based on our deliberately choosing a thought and holding its image in our mind. Simultaneously, we supply our own guided, positive mind-chatter in the form of such silently repeated phrases as "Every day in every way I am getting better and better."

The human brain is a biological computer that processes our thoughts. Input consists of stimuli from the outside world and from our own bodies brought in by our senses of smell, sight, touch, hearing, and taste. Input also consists of information that we obtain from conversations and from the media. Researchers have estimated that the brain receives more than forty thousand different stimuli every second, enough to overwhelm the most complex electronic computer.

All input is fed into the left hemisphere (the rational-thinking half) of the brain, where it is scanned by the mind's interpretive area. All incoming data are judged meaningful or filtered out as irrelevant. In this area of the brain, danger and alarm signals get priority. Threats of immediate physical danger trigger reflex motor actions that, for example, cause us to snatch a finger from a fire before it is burned. A nerve impulse from the finger races to a receptor in the upper spine where the reflex action is triggered. The impulse then continues into the mind's interpretive area. Here it is routed over priority pathways that prompt a thought of fire and danger to immediately pop up in the mind. This alarm thought instantly evokes a feeling of fear.

Less-urgent input is compared and matched with data held in the files of our belief system. Our brain's interpretive area responds with an appropriate thought based on how our belief system views the input data. For example, if we have just learned that a friend has landed a promotion that we had expected to get, this information is matched in our belief system with associations from the past. Based on the way we have learned to react to such news in the past, our interpretive area could choose a loving thought that makes us glad for our friend's success. Or it could choose a negative thought that, considering all the hard work we'd put in over the years without recognition, our friend was unfairly chosen for the job.

The thought that popped into our mind would evoke a feeling. A thought that our friend deserved success would evoke a positive feeling of happiness and love. A thought that we would rather have been chosen would evoke a negative feeling of injustice and envy.

Virtually every feeling we experience is preceded by a thought. The specific thought that we hold in our mind produces the specific way we feel. (Certain feelings appear to be provoked by hormones without a preceding thought, such as a feeling of well-being after having exercised. Drugs and dreams can also produce strong feelings.)

We Feel What We Think

A feeling or emotion (they are the same) is a physical reaction to a thought caused by chemical changes in the nerve cells in our mind-computer. We can be conscious of both the thought (as an image with its accompanying mind-chatter) and the feeling itself. It is entirely through our feelings that we experience life and live it. For instance, if our finger touches a hot burner, a reflex prompts us to snatch it away. But we cannot actually feel pain until a thought of pain pops into our mind. On this primitive level, the thought slips instantly into the mind through habitual response. Yet the thought of pain must enter the mind before pain can be felt.

Most of life's experiences are built on such positive emotions as love, joy, ecstasy, compassion, faith, hope, satisfaction, and gratitude, or on such negative emotions as fear, worry, anxiety, panic, hate, anger, and resentment. A thought invariably precedes each of these feelings.

We experience our feelings in the limbic area of the brain that surrounds the hypothalamus, which governs the action of all other glands in the body, including the pituitary, the master gland. The pituitary secretes hormones that enter the bloodstream and control every involuntary body function from kidney-urine action to the operation of the immune system, heart rate, blood pressure, and even growth.

The hypothalamus can be thought of as a two-way switch: one side is the calm state and the other is the fight-or-flight state. The body is always in one state or the other. Whenever a negative thought evokes a negative feeling, or even a borderline negative feeling such as unpleasantness, frustration, or uncertainty, the hypothalamus switches on the fight-or-flight state.

The fight-or-flight (hypermetabolic) state is a hair-trigger response that readies the body to meet instant physical danger, regardless of whether the body is in actual physical danger. The sympathetic nervous system, the emergency branch of the autonomic nervous system, takes over and all systems are go. Adrenaline and cortisone shoot into the bloodstream to speed up the body's functions, including heart rate, and to increase circulation. Autonomic nerve fibers, which parallel each blood vessel, signal the smooth muscles to constrict every artery and arteriole. Blood pressure shoots up. The stomach produces more acid than normal and blood is shunted from the digestive system to the brain and muscles. White blood cell production is cut back, suppressing the immune system and increasing susceptibility to infection.

The clotting ability of the blood improves in preparation for a possible wound and red cells pour into the bloodstream to carry additional oxygen to the muscles. Glycogen (sugar) is released from the liver, causing the blood sugar level to rise, and our muscles fill with energy and tense for action. Simultaneously, brain-wave activity speeds up to between 13 and 30 cycles per second and the brain enters the rational-thinking beta level.

This response, a legacy from our primitive brain, prepares us to combat or to flee from a physical danger that may no longer exist. It is unlearned behavior, an instinctive response to a threat to our survival.

The hypothalamus cannot distinguish whether a negative feeling such as fear is provoked by a charging elephant or by a letter saying we are overdrawn at the bank. Whether the danger is physical or emotional, the hypothalamus turns on the fight-or-flight reaction automatically as soon as we experience a negative feeling. Only the intensity of the reaction varies in direct proportion to the immediacy of the threat. A vague feeling of envy won't turn on the same intensity of alarm as would a confrontation with an armed thief. In the case of envy, the fight-or-flight reactions continue to smolder at low intensity until the negative feeling is released.

If we act out the fight-or-flight response by either fighting or fleeing (or by jogging or taking any similar form of vigorous exercise) we release the pent-up muscular tension and no harm is done to our body. But if, as is often true in modern society, physical action is impossible, we remain tense and we enter a state of physical distress. Repressing a negative emotion only

makes the fight-or-flight state harder to turn off. Many people live continuously in a low-level fight-or-flight state in which it is impossible ever to
experience genuine relaxation or calm.

The calm (hypometabolic) state is a relaxed condition of serenity and
peace. The parasympathetic branch of the autonomic nervous system takes
over and maintains routine metabolism. Blood lactate levels drop, tension
disappears, and negative thoughts and feelings are driven from the mind.
The heart rate drops, blood pressure falls, respiration slows, and oxygen
consumption is reduced by as much as 20 percent. The white blood cell
count increases and the immune system becomes better able to destroy
infections or cancer. Brain-wave activity drops to as low as 8 to 13 cycles
per second, at which point we enter the relaxed alpha state. In the alpha
state, our tolerance to pain increases significantly. We feel comfortable and
relaxed and enter a state of ease in which the whole person thrives.

The Dynamics of Stress

Most stress arises from life changes and problems related to job and
family, society and its institutions, or the image we have of ourselves. Such
sources of stress as the death of a spouse or loved one, or loss of a job,
money, or possessions have always been with us. But the pressure and
complexity of modern society have added new sources of stress—comput-
ers and machines replacing people, air and water pollution, crowded conditions in increasingly complex metropolitan centers, hurrying, meeting
deadlines and schedules, paying taxes, and dealing with government regu-
lations.

Several years ago Dr. Thomas Holmes and Dr. Richard Rahe of the University of Washington Medical School classified the average amount of
stress caused by a person's having to adjust to various life events (see chart,
page 31). A significant finding was that stressful life events are not necessarily all unpleasant. Stress can also be caused by such pleasant changes as
marriage, having a baby, winning or inheriting money, earning a promotion, or achieving an outstanding success.

Although the Holmes-Rahe rating measures the degree of adjustment
required by stressful life situations, social pressures such as freeway driving,
noise, crowded living conditions, poor lighting, crime, being late for work,
the pressure of meeting bills, or feeling lonely and unloved can all be highly
stressful.

Stress can be caused by envy of our neighbors' status as they acquire
more possessions, travel to exotic places, or join prestigious clubs. Advertising heightens stress by creating desire for fresh acquisitions that place additional burdens on our financial resources. Such is the complexity of

modern living that millions of Americans are overburdened with the problems of too many possessions, interests, and commitments, and too many tasks must be accomplished in a limited time.

For many people the most constant source of stress is the way in which we are endlessly bombarded by disturbing news carried by TV and newspapers. Most people spend each evening reviewing a composite of wars, famines, disasters, strikes, violent crimes, and shortages of fuel, food, and energy, often distorted out of all proportion to the effect they have on us personally.

Whether they exist in our hometown or halfway around the world, if we interpret these life events as harmful or threatening, they will trigger a negative thought, a negative feeling, and the fight-or-flight response. Whenever

---

Stress Rating of Social Readjustments

(Within each stress range, events are
listed in decreasing order of stress.)

Stress Range	Life Event
81–100	Death of spouse
71–80	Divorce
61–70	Marital separation; jail term; death of close family member
51–60	Personal illness or injury; marriage
41–50	Loss of job; marital conciliation; retirement; change in health of member of family; pregnancy
31–40	Sex problems; new family member; business readjustment; change in financial state; death of close friend; change to different type of work; change in number of arguments with spouse; assumption of substantial mortgage
21–30	Foreclosure of loan or mortgage; change in work responsibilities; son or daughter leaving home; difficulties with in-laws; outstanding personal achievement; spouse begins or stops work; beginning or end of school; change in living conditions; revision of lifestyle habits; difficulties with employer or supervisor
11–20	Change in working hours or conditions; change in residence; change in schools; change in recreation; change in church activities; change in social life; assumption of moderate-sized mortgage or loan; change in sleeping habits; change in frequency of family get-togethers; change in eating habits; vacation; Christmas; minor law violations

the fight-or-flight response remains unresolved, it eventually leads to stress and disease.

How Stress Triggers Disease

The link between stressful life events and such diseases as atherosclerosis, heart disease, hypertension, stroke, cancer, diabetes, kidney disease, ulcers, ulcerative colitis, obesity, and all infectious diseases is so clear that psychologists have been able to predict with a high degree of accuracy the risk of subsequent illness based on the amount of stress existing in a person's life. Using the Holmes-Rahe list of stress values, researchers have found that in any one year a total stress rating of 150 or less indicates a one-in-three risk of a serious illness occurring during the next thirty-six months; a rating of 150 to 300 indicates a one-in-two risk of a serious illness occurring during the next thirty-six months; and a rating of 300 or more indicates a 90 percent risk of a serious illness occurring during the next twenty-four months.

Supporting these statistics is a British study of the spouses of 490 people who died. In the year after bereavement, the death rate among the surviving spouses was ten times higher than among married people of comparable age and sex. Another study showed that divorced people become sick twelve times as frequently during the year following their divorce as do married people.

Stress is a shapeless destroyer of health that many medical researchers believe is the underlying cause of at least 80 percent of all human ailments and disease. Yet stress itself is a neutral factor. Stress is everywhere. Some stress is essential for growth and learning.

The way in which our mind-computer interprets life's changes and events largely determines whether we become sick. If our belief system is based on negative attitudes, we will respond to life events with a negative thought that trips a negative feeling, turns on the fight-or-flight response, and sends the whole body into an emergency state that, if sustained, is capable of causing almost every known disease. If our belief system is based on positive attitudes, we will interpret the same life event with a positive thought that trips a positive feeling, turns on the calm state, and sends our whole person into a relaxed condition that sustains high-level wellness.

All Diseases Are Stress-Related

Hans Selye, pioneer stress researcher at the University of Montreal, is credited with the discovery of the general adaptive syndrome. He found that after a person is faced with a stressful change and goes into a prolonged fight-or-flight state, the body undergoes a resistance period during which it adapts to change. But adjusting to a stressful change is often so demanding that the person is left exhausted.

Primarily, this exhaustion is due to prolonged muscular tension that persists as long as one remains in the fight-or-flight state. Since repressed negative emotions can keep a person in a low-level fight-or-flight state indefinitely, the sustained muscular tension saps the person's energy, causing typical stress-related conditions such as chronic fatigue, tension headaches, or backache.

Millions of Americans live in a permanent state of emergency with their muscles in a constant state of contraction, waiting for a physical fight-or-flight action that never comes. As long as a person's belief system continues to interpret life's events as harmful, negative thoughts dominate the mind, and the sympathetic nervous system keeps all body systems keyed up to a state of emergency readiness. The heart continues to beat faster, blood pressure stays elevated, stomach acidity and blood sugar levels remain high, digestive functions are impaired, and the disease-fighting powers of the immune system remain suppressed.

When these abnormal conditions are sustained, one or more of the following disease states eventually occurs.

Suppression of the immune system. Our ability to stay free of cancer and all infectious diseases, including virus and bacteria, depends on the number and aggressiveness of the white cells in the bloodstream. Each person has approximately 126 billion lymphocyte cells, all produced in the marrow of our larger bones. Approximately half of the lymphocytes we produce pass through the thymus gland where they are endowed with the functions of T cells. The remaining lymphocytes function as B cells.

T cells patrol the bloodstream, seeking out invading bacteria, viruses, and other foreign cells. The T cells recognize each cell they encounter by the antigen code on the cell's surface. When our own cells mutate and become cancer cells, their antigen changes so that T cells recognize them as foreign. The average person probably produces a hundred or more cancer cells every day from exposure to carcinogens, cosmic rays, or X rays. When a T cell meets a cancer cell or invading bacteria, it memorizes that cell's antigen. The T cell then hastens to the nearest lymph node, where it alerts T cells to attack the invader.

The messenger T cell also alerts all B cells. As it touches each B cell with the foreign cell's memorized antigen, each B cell commences production of antibodies that can recognize the invader's antigen and attack it.

Giant macrophage cells are also alerted and these too converge on the foreign cell. Within a few minutes the target cell is attacked by cells, antibodies, and macrophages, all squirting destructive enzymes that eat a hole in its outer wall and kill it. This is the body's immune system effectively at work.

Cancer, as well as most infectious diseases, can survive in the body only when our T cells fail to recognize the antigen of a cell as foreign. This may occur because of immunological overload during a bout of disease such as pneumonia, in which case the number of invading pneumonia bacteria plus cancer cells may overwhelm the immune system's capacity to destroy them. It can also occur if the thymus gland becomes atrophied as a result of life-style risk factors such as failing to exercise, indulging in a high-fat diet, or smoking cigarettes. When this happens, which is almost routine in sedentary persons and heavy smokers, the number of T cells declines, antibodies become weak, and the body eventually succumbs to an infection or cancer.

Suppression of the immune system is also a function of the fight-or-flight state. During this state, imbalance in hormone production also can stimulate formation and growth of malignant tumors. Whenever the body remains tensed in an emergency state for a prolonged period, our resistance declines and we become susceptible to cancer, pneumonia, rheumatoid arthritis, rheumatic heart disease, multiple sclerosis, ulcerative colitis, and similar types of autoimmune or infectious diseases. (Autoimmunity is a dysfunction of the immune system in which our lymphocytes, which are supposed to protect us, begin to harass our own body cells and tissue.)

Supporting the evidence that stress causes many of our diseases is the fact that people who are retarded or mentally disturbed seldom get cancer. After studying 3,214 deaths reported by the Texas Department of Mental Health and Mental Retardation, a University of Texas research team discovered that cancer was responsible for only 4 percent of deaths compared to 18 percent among the general population. Even though many of the people in the study smoked or ate a high-fat diet containing carcinogens, the researchers believed that a mental disorder, in which stress is not an everyday occurrence, protects people from suppression of their immune system. In comparison, paranoid patients who are constantly fearful of the people and events around them have an above-average cancer rate.

Hardening of the arteries and cardiovascular disease. A survey that found that the cholesterol level of tax accountants always rose in April is one of many studies to demonstrate that stress is capable of increasing a person's cholesterol level. The body's blood cholesterol level is largely controlled by the endocrine/hormone system, in which an imbalance occurs whenever the body is in the fight-or-flight state.

Cholesterol is carried through the bloodstream by its lipoprotein fraction. When under stress we often tend to overeat, especially foods rich in saturated fats. One result of a high-fat diet is an increase in the proportion of low density lipoproteins (LDLs). LDLs carry cholesterol into the arteries, where the cholesterol forms plaques that constrict the lumen or inner diameter of the arteries and reduce blood flow. Risk of arterial blockage is increased as stress-induced hormonal changes cause tears to develop in artery walls. These tears soon fill with cholesterol plaques. Cigarette smoking and lack of exercise also contribute to constriction and blockage of the arteries, a condition known as atherosclerosis or hardening of the arteries.

High density lipoproteins (HDLs), by contrast, carry cholesterol out of the arteries and excrete it through the liver. Exercise, a high-fiber diet of natural foods, and positive thoughts (the wellness equation) stimulate production of HDLs, which reduce the blood cholesterol level.

Blockage of a leg artery by cholesterol plaques can cause claudication (unbearable leg pains with risk of amputation). Blockage of a coronary artery can restrict blood flow to the heart muscle, causing severe angina pain and, eventually, a heart attack.

As cholesterol plaques reduce the volume of a person's blood vessels, blood pressure is forced higher. Blood pressure also increases as the sympathetic nervous system causes the smooth muscles that surround each artery to squeeze and constrict the artery. Elevated blood pressure (hypertension) is therefore commonly associated with prolonged occurrence of the fight-or-flight response. To overcome the increased peripheral resistance of the arteries, the heart must work harder and pump more blood. Over an extended period, hypertension heightens the risk of premature heart attack, stroke, or kidney damage.

So sensitive are our vasoconstrictor muscles to stress that blood pressure will rise whenever a stressful stimulus reaches the mind or even when a stressful event is discussed in conversation. Conversely, whenever a person expresses and releases deep feelings about these same stressful topics, blood pressure drops.

Most hypertensives bear deeply repressed anger, resentment, or fear but cover up their inner hostility by assuming an outwardly restrained and nonchalant appearance. The resulting inner conflict reinforces their stress, sending their blood pressure even higher.

But stress can cause a heart attack even in the absence of atherosclerosis or hypertension. Fifteen percent of all deaths from heart attack are actually caused by rhythmic heart disturbance triggered by imbalance in the hypothalamus and autonomic nervous system resulting from a prolonged period in the fight-or-flight state. As tension overloads the nervous system's circuitry, a person may experience irregular or missed heartbeats, extra heartbeats, palpitation, or ventricular fibrillation (an often fatal runaway heartbeat as the interpretive area of the brain is excited by stress). Rhythmic heart disturbances often disappear after exercise because physical activity releases the muscular tension that creates the overload in the nervous system.

Stomach acidity and ulcer formation. Under control of the hypothalamus, the autonomic nervous system regulates production of pepsin and stomach acid. Numerous studies including the classic study by G. F. Mahl and associates, which related the stress of approaching exams to an increase in stomach acidity among students, have proved that ulcers are almost always caused by prolonged occurrence of the fight-or-flight state.

Under stress, pepsinogen, a normally harmless pre-enzyme found in the stomach, becomes a caustic and corrosive acid that eats into the mucous lining of the stomach and small intestines. Each year, in this way, stress literally eats a hole in the intestines of millions of Americans. And as every ulcer sufferer knows, the pain increases in direct proportion to the stress.

Kidney and urinary tract dysfunction. Under direct control of the hypothalamus is the pituitary gland, which secretes an antidiuretic hormone (that is, one that suppresses urination), and the adrenal cortex, which produces hormones that regulate the body's fluid level and urine production. Thus the kidneys and urinary system are highly sensitive to negative emotions.

Almost invariably, people who urinate excessively—a condition known as diuresis—have continual anxious or aggressive feelings. Other people with deeply repressed resentment, hostility, or frustration often suffer from engorgement and inflammation of the bladder. In both conditions, infection is usually not present and the frequent urination is caused directly by negative emotions that result in stress.

Obesity and diabetes. Close to the hypothalamus are two centers controlling hunger and satisfaction. As the blood sugar level falls, the hunger center is chemically stimulated. After a person has eaten, the blood sugar level rises and turns off the hunger center while simultaneously turning on the satisfaction center.

But people who live continuously in the fight-or-flight state often discover that they can temporarily soothe the distress of tension by stimulating the satisfaction center by continuing to eat beyond the point at which their hunger ends. This compulsive eating also eases distress arising from feeling anxious, fearful, angry, unloved, unwanted, or frustrated.

As they learn to eat for pleasure and entertainment rather than just to satisfy hunger, compulsive eaters become passive, helpless people unable to control their own bodies. Any additional stress sends them heading for the refrigerator. Obesity becomes a way of life, and with it comes increased risk of hypoglycemia, heart disease, hypertension, and adult-onset diabetes. All these diseases worsen in direct proportion to the degree of stress existing in a person's life.

Other common stress-related diseases include some forms of asthma, acne, anemia, constipation, edema, eczema, hay fever, headaches, hyperthyroidism, and fever blisters. Backache is frequently caused by intense and sustained contraction of the lower back muscles resulting from the fight-or-flight state.

Negative Thoughts Lead to Negative Behavior

In one way or another, virtually all human ailments are precipitated by stress. Disease begins when a person's belief system programs his or her mind-computer to interpret life events as threatening and unfriendly. This evokes a negative thought and a negative feeling and causes the hypothalamus to turn on the fight-or-flight response. The tension caused by this response leads to negative behavior. People seek release from tension and distress by smoking, consuming alcohol and caffeine, eating junk foods and high-risk foods, abandoning exercise, taking drugs, and generally abusing their bodies. If a cluster of stressful events occurs within a short period, it can strain the nervous system and block arteries, suppress the immune system, burn a hole in the stomach, or trigger a heart attack, stroke, or the onset of cancer, diabetes, rheumatoid arthritis, gout, ulcer, or other chronic or infectious disease.

A negative thought triggers negative body chemistry. But as the pain clinics have demonstrated, it is also true that what the mind can cause, the mind can reverse and heal.

How Inner Healing Works

Inner healing techniques are designed to intervene in the disease process by allowing us to:

Stop a negative thought dead in its tracks and replace it instantly with a positive thought.

Train the mind to select a positive thought in response to a stressful situation instead of a health-destroying negative thought.

Reprogram our belief system so that the mind sees the world as a beautiful, friendly place and interprets almost all potentially stressful events as harmless learning experiences or interesting adventures.

Transform the fight-or-flight state into the calm state in as brief a time as one minute.

Use guided imagery to place in the mind powerful and carefully selected positive thoughts and images depicting our recovery from disease as a message to the body to restore wellness.

3. How to Liberate Yourself from Emotional Stress

BOB CORRELLI had been convalescing from pneumonia for weeks. His recovery was so slow that his doctor sent him to a small hot-springs convalescent center in New Mexico to recuperate.

The chiropractor in charge of the center believed in treating the whole person, not just the lungs. It didn't take him long to learn that a few months earlier Bob had found out that he was being considered for promotion to manager of the bank where he worked. As the weeks went by nothing happened and finally Bob experienced bitter disappointment and contracted pneumonia.

The chiropractor told Bob that his illness had probably been triggered by stress when the world had failed to conform to his expectations. Bob had placed all his expectations on being promoted within a short time, and when his expectations were not fulfilled, he experienced intensely negative emotions and increasing stress.

The chiropractor taught Bob a technique that would take the stress out of most potentially stressful life events. First, Bob was to place on his mental movie screen his *expectation* that he would be promoted. Then he was to slide this thought off his inner screen and replace it with the thought that he would *rather* be promoted. The point of this exercise was that if Bob was not promoted after all he would not suffer any emotional letdown because he has not built up any premature expectations. Since Bob would merely rather be promoted, he would remain happy and content regardless of what happened.

The chiropractor persuaded Bob to live one day at a time without building up any expectations or desires that could trigger a negative thought and a negative emotion if they weren't fulfilled. Each time a desire or expectation arose, Bob would mentally transform it into a *rather-belief*. When any other type of negative thought appeared, Bob would simply pinch his wrist, call out "stop," slide the thought aside, and replace it with an image of a beautiful garden.

At first all this took a lot of Bob's attention. He had to constantly remind himself to transform all his desires and expectations into rather-beliefs and to stop any negative thought by replacing it with a positive one. Bob found that his mind responded to exercise and training just like his body did. Reprogramming his beliefs did take some inner work, but at the end of the first day Bob felt better than he had in weeks.

The memory of the first day's success served to keep him thinking positively. By the seventh day he was instinctively thinking positive thoughts all of the time. At this point Bob suddenly discovered that all symptoms of pneumonia had vanished and he felt perfectly fit and strong.

Negative Thoughts Create Disease-Prone Personalities

Bob's character traits class him as a Type C personality. Under stress, Type C's experience a sustained fight-or-flight state that stimulates production of cortisone-type hormones by the adrenal glands. The cortisone suppresses the immune system and Type C's become susceptible to cancer, arthritis, pneumonia, and other infectious diseases, as well as to depression and obesity.

About two decades ago San Francisco cardiologists Meyer Friedman and Ray H. Rosenman conducted a long-term study of 2,750 men in an attempt to relate personality traits to heart disease. They classified approximately 50 percent of the men as Type A's: aggressive, hard-driving human dynamos ruled by the clock and obsessed with trying to accomplish more and more in less and less time. Forty percent were classified as Type B's: relaxed, easygoing people who cultivate calm, optimism, and moderation. The remaining 10 percent fell in between.

Over a period of eight and a half years, the incidence of heart disease was three times greater for Type A's than for Type B's. And when a heart attack did occur, it proved fatal twice as often for Type A's as for Type B's.

More recently, other researchers have classified a Type C or cancer-prone personality. Let's briefly review these personality models.

Type A's have an aggressive personality that externalizes stress in the form of cardiovascular disease (atherosclerosis, heart attack, stroke), hypertension, diabetes, and migraine or tension headaches. Type A's want to act aggressively but often cannot because of social restrictions; hence they hide their hostility behind a calm and nonchalant exterior. As a result, they often have deeply repressed anxiety, anger, guilt, or envy.

Type C's repress all negative feelings to the point where they become unable to express emotions or discharge tension. This internalized stress may suppress the immune system and can result in cancer, infectious diseases, or rheumatoid arthritis. If the person is particularly shy and dependent, disease often appears in the digestive tract as gallstones, colitis, ulcerative colitis, ulcers and gastritis, or as chronic constipation or diarrhea.

Type C's are dependent personalities who try to appear outwardly calm, sweet, gentle, and nice while inwardly they are often resentful and unforgiving, worried and anxious, bored, frustrated, and apathetic. Type C's frequently feel helpless, passive, useless, unworthy, rejected, and abandoned. They often experience guilt and despair. To try to win love, they try to please everyone. They abandon their goals and place the needs of others before their own; they become human doormats. They depend for happiness on external factors such as marriage, parenthood, or job. When a spouse dies, children leave home, or a job is lost, they experience such stress that they often succumb to a disease within six to twelve months.

The strain of internal conflict—of appearing to be what they are not—saps their energy and also prevents their becoming completely open and truthful. They abandon hope and give up the will to live. Many Type C's have an inability to develop and maintain close relationships, and their marital and sexual relationships tend to be unsatisfactory. Research shows that they have lacked close human skin contact (hugging) throughout their lives. Even though they seek affection, they tend to reject it when it is offered. If they experience disappointment in one personal relationship, they give up hope and will seldom try again. A high proportion of Type C's are divorced or living alone.

Recognize yourself? If so, you will probably want to change from a self-destructive Type A or C personality to a well-adjusted Type B. Type B's are relaxed and seldom hurry but they are in full control of their lives and they often accomplish more than the excessively time-scheduled Type A's.

Though Type B's have worthwhile goals, their drives and ambitions are less urgent, they are resistant to stress, and they are genuinely independent, optimistic, positive, and cheerful. If they do experience a negative emotion, they release it at the first opportunity. For instance, the average Type B male feels no shame at crying in public should the situation demand it.

One way a Type A or C person can become a Type B is by reprogramming his or her belief system through the inner healing methods described in this book. As you change your philosophy of life and adopt a more holistic approach to health, you will find that your diseases and ailments will disappear along with your negative emotions and stress.

Ready? You can begin with three techniques designed to eliminate most of the negative thoughts and feelings that destroy the health of Type A and C personalities.

INNER HEALING TECHNIQUE #1
How to Develop Instant Health-Building Win-Power

This easy technique makes it as simple to change to a positive state of mind as it is to switch to another TV channel. If you're like most people, and especially if you're a Type C, you'll probably find yourself resisting change with every cell, thought, and muscle in your body. After all, it's always easier, safer, and more secure not to change at all. Change is stressful and there's no guarantee you'll be happy if you do change. We've all heard the excuses.

"It won't work."

"I haven't time."

"I'm too old to change."

"Not today, perhaps next week."

"My health is too poor."

"I can't help it. This is the way I am."

"I've always been this way."

And so on. How do people psych themselves up to overcome these excuses? We all know that when people are ready to change, they will change. The truth is that at any moment you can decide to step out of your A or C personality and start becoming a disease-resistant Type B.

How? By switching on your win-power mind state. In just a few seconds, at any time, you can transform yourself from a helpless, dependent, passive, disease-prone being to a dedicated, determined person committed to winning wellness.

Begin by thinking of something at which you excel, something at which you know you can succeed. All of us have something we're good at, whether it's playing the harmonica or hiking up a mountain peak or cutting a figure on roller skates or painting in oils or creative writing. It doesn't have to be anything great or dramatic. It can be something as simple as walking.

If you can ride a ten-speed bicycle thirty-five miles, you know you could cover forty miles next time. You know that, if challenged, nothing, absolutely nothing, could stop you from riding forty miles on your ten-speed. You believe and you know you would succeed. You are absolutely certain you would succeed. (Whatever you excel at, substitute it for the bicycle in this example.)

Make a vivid picture in your mind of yourself on your ten-speed. See the glitter of spinning wheels, hear the soft hum of tires on the road, feel the wind in your face as you pedal down a country lane, smell the rich aroma of fresh-cut hay as you pass each farm, touch your derailleur levers, and see how responsive and sensitive your bike is.

Now analyze and identify the state of mind you are in. Experience it. Know what it feels like. Realize that in this state of mind you can accomplish anything. In this state of mind virtually all battles and races were won and giant mountains were conquered. People have used this state of mind to overcome every kind of illness and ailment.

We aren't talking about trying. Try to pick up a 200-pound bag of corn. You either pick it up or it stays on the ground. Trying is just another cause for excuses.

Trying has no place in the win-power mind state. You're going to win. Nothing, absolutely nothing, can stop you from succeeding. You are absolutely certain you can succeed. Given time, you can attain any achievable goal. You know you can win because you are depending entirely on yourself. You know that the only way to succeed is to be a self-starter, to make use of your own resourcefulness, to help yourself—and to *go for it!*

Now slide the thought-image of the bicycle (or whatever it is that you excel at) off your inner movie screen and replace it with an image of whatever health problem you want to overcome.

All your original confidence, optimism, persistence, determination, and dedication to winning are still there as you confront a totally new goal.

Let's say you have a peptic ulcer that is making life miserable and you're willing to do anything to heal it. Begin by visualizing your ulcer on your inner movie screen. As you see it, make a silent commitment that more than anything else in the world you want your ulcer to heal and vanish. Feel the win-power surge within you as you commit yourself to give top priority in your life to healing your ulcer.

Win-power isn't something you can use in a casual, halfhearted way. Overcoming your ulcer is now the most important thing in your life. There's nothing weak, passive, or helpless about your commitment to winning back new health. Your new win-power mind state is the very opposite of the typical helpless Type C personality that succumbs to cancer. With all the zeal of a health crusader you now have a burning desire to achieve total wellness.

Pause and analyze your win-power mind state. You are totally and completely dedicated to healing your ulcer and you are determined to take an active role in your own recovery.

Nothing can stand in the way of your success. Sure, change is sometimes difficult. Reversing the outdated beliefs that caused the stress that gave you the ulcer requires mental effort and inner work.

Yet it is often easier to do than to read about. Though each day your progress may seem imperceptible, what seemed impossible on the day you began often becomes a reality within just two or three weeks.

Age is no barrier. Given reasonably good circulation, the human mind ages more slowly than any other organ. But without constant use and exercise, the mind will atrophy like any body muscle. Old age begins only when we cease mentally growing and learning. We grow only as we update and improve our belief system. The day we grow old is the day we stop shedding old outworn beliefs and replacing them with newer, more effective ones. It's never too late to change, unless you give up.

Implementing new beliefs requires mental exercise and training comparable to the physical exercise and training we use to rebuild our bodies. As the mind learns to use new nerve pathways, new ways of believing and thinking suddenly become second nature just as we once suddenly discovered we could swim or ride a bicycle after days or weeks of practice.

After a few practice sessions, you will find you can psych yourself up with win-power in less than one minute. The more often you enter the win-power state of mind, the easier it will be to stay in this exuberant mind state all the time.

INNER HEALING TECHNIQUE #2
The Sudden-Stop Way to Cancel Out Stress

Remember how stress causes disease? When your belief system interprets a life event as threatening or unfriendly, your mind locates a negative thought and places it on your inner movie screen. This sets off a negative emotion and the fight-or-flight response with its chain of negative body reactions. Over a prolonged period, negative body chemistry can lead to almost any ailment or disease.

You will know when your mind interprets something as stressful because this is the point at which you start feeling upset. Although the fight-or-flight response is already triggered, no real harm has been done yet at this stage.

At the *first hint* of any feeling that threatens to upset you, boldly take the following steps.

1. Pinch your wrist hard and call out "Stop! Stop!" (Do this silently if others are around.)

2. Take a deep breath as you visualize the figure 10. Take another deep breath as you visualize the figure 9. Slowly continue counting back to zero, holding each figure in your mind's eye as you take a deep breath and exhale.

3. Pause for a few moments while you review the situation that is making you emotionally upset. Recall and focus on the negative thought that triggered the negative feeling. Decide on an assertive, positive thought that is the exact opposite of the negative thought. Slide the negative thought aside and replace it on your inner movie screen with the positive thought you

44

have just chosen. Continue to hold this positive image in your mind. (If you have been unable to choose a positive thought, slide in an image of a calm, beautiful garden or beach scene. Either way, the new positive thought will create a new, positive feeling of calm and love.)

4. Relax while your hypothalamus turns off the fight-or-flight state and switches to the calm state. Alternate the positive thought with an image of yourself calm, relaxed, and in perfect health.

5. Review all the good things that are going on in your life. Feel gratitude for all these good things.

6. Roll your shoulders around and up and down. Then let your head go completely limp and roll it slowly around in a complete circle, six times one way and six times the other way. After that, tense each muscle in the body one at a time, hold for eight seconds, then release. This will release all unresolved tension that built up during the brief period your body was in the fight-or-flight state. Any additional physical exercise would also be beneficial.

Although this technique does not actually reprogram your belief system, it will abruptly halt the stress-disease process the moment it begins. Use the stop technique immediately whenever you experience an upsetting thought or feeling. Excluding the neck roll, you can often use all six steps while at work or in a public place without anyone's being aware of what you are doing.

If you are regularly upset by the same disturbing life event, record the entire sudden-stop technique out loud on a cassette tape. Keep the tape cued in, ready to play. The moment you experience the upsetting feeling, sit or lie down and turn on the tape.

To ensure swift operation of the sudden-stop technique, you should consciously choose in advance one or more assertive, positive thoughts that are the exact opposite of the type of disturbing thought you experience most often. For example, if news about a recession in the newspapers has triggered a thought that you might lose your job, replace it with a scene in which a dozen job recruiters are lined up, each ready to offer you an interesting, well-paid job.

We are free to choose our own thoughts, and we can determine the kinds of thoughts our mind-computer selects for us. Our happiness doesn't depend on events, situations, or people in the outside world. Since a thought must precede each emotion we feel, we can choose to feel any way we desire to feel by simply choosing an appropriate thought.

We should always be prepared with a thought-image of a beautiful garden or beach scene or some scene or image that makes us feel loving and calm. Practice visualizing a garden or beach caressed by a gentle breeze, with a blue sky overhead, and the whole scene filled with brilliant sunshine. Smell the salty ocean or the rich earth. Feel the sun's warm, therapeutic rays. Touch the sand or grass under you. Experience the complete calm and the total lack of stress in the scene. Decide in advance exactly what flowers or distant sailboats or other calming influences you would like in your scene.

If you have trouble visualizing a complex scene like a beach or garden, simply visualize a handsome jar or vase, or a single flower or painting you like. Anything will do, provided you can conjure up the image instantly and your mind enjoys the image more than the thought you are displacing.

Rather than pinching his wrist, one eighty-year-old man wears a rubber band around his wrist and snaps it to start the sudden-stop process. He says out loud, "I've had enough!" Then he slides the offending thought out of his mind and replaces it with a beautiful beach or garden scene.

You can carry the sudden-stop technique one step further by writing down a brief description of the event that causes a negative thought each time one occurs. Keep a record of events in your life that your mind interprets as stressful. Analyze and classify them. Very rarely are there more than fifteen stressful themes, often not more than ten.

Make a list of these stressful themes and assign each a number. As soon as a negative thought enters your mind, identify it and call out loudly, "Here's number nine again." Visualize a huge figure 9 superimposed on the negative thought. Then slide the negative thought aside and replace it with a positive thought. After a few more attempts to break into your mind, number nine will give up.

This technique is particularly effective for negative thoughts that trigger worry and that release a flood of worrisome mind-chatter. As you slide the negative thought off your inner movie screen and replace it with a positive thought, the mind-chatter will disappear.

A variation on the thought-stopping technique is to visualize yourself putting a blowtorch to the negative thought-image and burning it up. Each time it comes back on your inner movie screen, set fire to it. See it go up in flames. Several of my acquaintances report that this is one of the most effective ways to eliminate persistent negative thoughts.

Our Primitive Beliefs Are out of Step with Modern Times

Perhaps because our mind-computer comes without an owner's manual, most of us have trouble learning to use it properly. In the dim dawn of early history the mind served as a primitive survival mechanism. It reasoned out where to find food and shelter, and when danger threatened it turned on the fight-or-flight response. Our modern brain has a much larger cortex and more complex reasoning powers than our ancestors' brain, but our minds today retain much of that primitive, instinctual capacity. In fact, our minds are still dominated by things we fear and by things we desire; by our own need to survive and to be secure; and by our need to make the world conform to our wishes. In other words, we are still dominated by primitive instincts.

As humans became civilized, our exposure to physical danger decreased, but there are new alarm situations in the stresses and problems of daily living. Those stressful situations switch on the fight-or-flight response, producing the same fear and tension that our ancestors experienced in the jungle. But since it is often impossible in modern society to release tension by fighting or by running away, the fight-or-flight response now causes a repression of those instincts and is a threat to our health and happiness.

Most of us are living in modern society programmed by primitive instincts that were necessary for survival millions of years ago in a primitive environment. The thoughts and efforts of the majority of people in Western industrialized society are devoted to survival (achieved through money and security); to ego-power (achieved through possessions, education, knowledge, status, prestige, and ego buildup through proving how right we are and how wrong others are); and sensory pleasures (achieved through sexual relationships, physical comfort, and eating).

The plain fact is that most people with Type A and C personalities are programmed by primitive instincts that simply don't work in modern society. They believe that they can achieve happiness only by pursuing more and more money, ego-power, and sensual pleasures. Yet virtually everyone who seeks these goals fails to achieve happiness and becomes dissatisfied with life. Almost everyone who measures success in material terms soon learns that life is an endless struggle that produces only fear, anger, resentment, envy, worry, and other negative emotions that lead to disease and shorten our lives. In what is probably a contemporary example of evolution—that is, survival of the fittest—Type A and C personalities die prematurely by the millions every year while Type B's tend to enjoy glowing good health and longer life.

Instead of being consumed by seeking security through money and power through possessions, the majority of Type B personalities are well-adjusted men and women who accept the world as it is, who love themselves and others, and who are prepared to share their time, money, and possessions with those less fortunate. These enlightened Type B's realize that happiness and pleasure are not goals to be actively pursued but are simply by-products of satisfying activities such as loving, sharing, giving, being open and truthful, nurturing, and enjoying satisfying relationships. Instead of measuring success in dollars and material possessions and view-

47

ing other people as threats and rivals, enlightened Type B's measure success by the number of satisfying personal relationships they experience and by the amount of good they can do. Being in control of their lives, they are free to choose positive thoughts that trigger positive emotions and they live in a relaxed, calm, happy, and contented state almost all of the time.

By contrast, most Type A and C personalities have been programmed all their lives by a belief system destined to make them sick and unhappy.

Certainly not all Type B's are run by highly evolved programming. But most people who enjoy robust health and who outlive their peers *are* among those more enlightened Type B's who have traded in their primitive programming for less damaging beliefs.

These Type B's are not impractical dreamers who shun work and responsibility; but they are realistic in realizing that once their basic needs for food, shelter, and other necessities have been provided for, the only way to achieve genuine happiness is to live by a more enlightened belief system.

How to Transform Primitive Expectations into Rather-Beliefs

Much of our stress and unhappiness can be directly traced to our primitive expectations of how things, people, and events in the world should be. When our expectations are unfulfilled because the world fails to conform, we find ourselves upset by negative thoughts and negative emotions.

A primitive expectation is a desire or demand that if not fulfilled triggers a negative emotion like anger, fear, envy, resentment, hate, or worry. When a primitive expectation is not fulfilled, we undergo a stressful change.

Suppose Jones loans his brother $500 to prevent a foreclosure on his house. The brother agrees to repay the loan in ninety days. Since Jones expects his brother to repay the loan on time, he is upset when his brother fails to do so. Now Jones must cancel his own vacation plans, a stressful change that makes him quite unhappy.

If Jones were a more enlightened Type B personality, how would he avoid the stress in this common life event? He would do so by transforming his primitive expectation into a rather-belief (which is shorthand for rather-be-healthy belief). Instead of expecting his brother to repay the loan on time, he would rather his brother repaid on time.

The difference between a primitive expectation and a rather-belief is quite profound. If Jones's expectation that his brother repay on time is not fulfilled, Jones reacts with a negative emotion that immediately arouses anger and resentment at his brother, plus fear and worry that he may never see his $500 again.

But if Jones would rather his brother repay the loan on time and if his brother fails to repay the loan, Jones's mind-computer interprets the information as harmless and it flows through his mind without producing a negative thought or negative feeling.

A rather-belief is something you would rather see happen. But if it fails to happen, you don't become emotionally upset and sick because you weren't expecting it to happen anyway. When a situation fails to work out the way you would rather it work out, you simply continue to flow along with the stream of life and you remain calm, loving, happy, and healthy.

This doesn't mean you need give up all your interests and possessions. You simply view them in a different way. Although you may currently own a home, a car, and a boat, you should not expect to always have them. What counts is not what we own but the use we make of possessions to enrich our lives, to help others, and to help us grow. You would rather continue having your possessions, but if through some unforeseen change—an economic crash, an energy shortage, a divorce settlement, a theft, or even a war or socialist revolution—you lose your possessions, you would not view the loss as stressful or upsetting.

This single change in your attitude can do more to make your life satisfying and to eliminate emotional stress and ill health than any other single change you can make.

All you need to do is simply transform into a rather-belief any primitive expectation that if not fulfilled will arouse a negative emotion. Whenever you feel tense or upset or experience a negative emotion, it is very probably being caused by an unfulfilled primitive expectation.

At least 80 percent of all human unhappiness and ill health is the result of outdated beliefs that cause us to see the world not as it is, but as we expect it to be. By liberating yourself from all primitive expectations, you will have taken a giant step toward eliminating all stress, unhappiness, sickness, and disease from your life.

Instead of becoming upset about potentially stressful life events, you will find yourself harmonizing with the events and flowing along with them. For instance, instead of becoming upset because inflation and recession are destroying your financial expectations, you simply flow along with inflation and recession and accept the world the way it is.

Eventually, you can be liberated from expecting things to turn out the way you want them to. You can find that nothing is either right or wrong, and you will find you have created a stress-free life in which nothing can go wrong or upset you.

4. How to Develop a Disease-Resistant Personality

GOOD HEALTH is not just having a blood pressure of 120 over 80 and normal results to a battery of diagnostic tests. What really constitutes good health is how successfully your life works. True wellness can be measured only by the health of the whole person: by how successfully you function in your job and your environment, by whether you are doing what you want to do and becoming the person you want to become, and by the number of satisfying relationships you have.

Recent studies at Cambridge Hospital in Massachusetts, Johns Hopkins Hospital, and Cornell Medical Center have separately confirmed that developing a stress-free Type B personality has greater influence on your health and longevity than either exercise or diet.

That good inner health is an essential prerequisite for good physical health was also confirmed by a forty-year Harvard study of 204 men aged twenty-one to forty-six. Of the fifty-nine men having the best mental health, only two had died or become chronically ill by age fifty-three. But of the forty-eight who showed the most worry, depression, and emotional stress, eighteen had died or become chronically ill by age fifty-three. The researchers concluded that poor inner health was more destructive to physical health than were smoking or being overweight.

How well our lives work depends on our mindset, which is the term used by psychologists to describe how our beliefs have programmed us to view the world. Our mindset determines how we make choices, how we interpret life events, how we feel, and how we believe and act.

Most people's minds are set to believe that we are not responsible for our own feelings. Our whole culture encourages us to depend for our happiness on people, things, and events outside ourselves. From infancy we have been conditioned to expect our happiness to depend on how another person acts, on what someone says or feels, or on how a certain situation turns out.

All this is primitive programming. Happiness comes from within. We feel happy when we choose to place a productive, joyful thought in our mind-computer. Thus a first step in changing our mindset is to transform into a rather-belief the primitive expectation that outside events will make us happy. Instead, we would *rather* that external events make us happy, but if they don't we can still be happy by choosing thoughts that make us feel good.

This chapter describes how you can build a disease-resistant Type B personality by transforming the most common primitive expectations into rather-beliefs. As you do, you will find that instead of becoming upset about stressful everyday events, you will blend in with the events and flow effortlessly along with them.

To do so, whenever you experience the onset of a negative emotion or a feeling of tension or upset, simply focus your awareness on the primitive expectation that is causing it. Then slide this expectation off your inner movie screen and replace it with a new rather-belief.

For instance, Laura Corrigan became extremely upset when, contrary to her expectations, her daughter ran off with a penniless artist and became his common-law wife. Whenever she thought about it, Laura's blood pressure soared and she suffered splitting headaches.

After consulting a counselor schooled in Rational Emotive Therapy, Laura learned to transform her expectation into a rather-belief. Though she would rather her daughter had married a financially successful man, the fact that her daughter had not done so was no longer going to make her sick. By canceling out her destructive expectation, Laura was able to reduce her blood pressure to a normal level and her headaches disappeared. She was actually transforming positive stress into negative stress. As a result the stressful event in Laura's life simply became nonstressful.

All it takes to turn stress to your advantage is to keep reminding yourself to do it.

INNER HEALING TECHNIQUE #3
Self-Remembering

G. I. Gurdjieff, the Russian esoteric psychologist and an early holistic health pioneer, found that most people failed to change their personalities for the better because they simply forgot their good intentions. Gurdjieff and many others discovered that, as long as we can keep reminding ourselves of our inner goals, making the required inner changes is comparatively easy.

The problem is that our ego prefers things the way they are. It resists change by allowing us to become distracted. During much of the day we conveniently forget our avowed intention to remove stress from our lives and to upgrade our personality.

Self-remembering is a conscious effort to remind yourself that whenever you feel threatened by stressful stimuli or by recurring primitive expectations, you are completely free to choose your response. You can consciously remind yourself at regular intervals that you are completely free to choose your own thoughts, which are in turn responsible for the way you feel and the way you behave. Remind yourself that outside events do not make you feel good or bad. It is what you believe about events, or about other people's attitudes, that creates a negative or positive feeling. If you believe that people usually want to hurt you, then you are likely to interpret other people's communications with you as hurtful and you will feel hurt. If you believe that people are basically kind and supportive, you will tend to interpret the same communications as positive, and you will feel calm and loving.

You simply keep reminding yourself, for example, to replace old, habitual primitive expectations with new rather-beliefs that cannot harm you. Normally you need only implant the seed thoughts of any new values or beliefs. Gradually your mind-computer will accept them and use them to overlay and blot out the destructive expectations.

You don't have to stay constantly alert. But whenever you feel threatened by stress, or feel that something is about to make you tense or upset, focus your attention on the offending expectation and mentally transform it into a rather-belief.

Self-remembering is an effective way to remind yourself to use the inner healing techniques that you know throughout the day. You can also use any kind of device that will prompt you to self-remember. Both men and women have found that by dressing in an entirely new way, they are constantly reminded by their unfamiliar attire of their new inner purpose. If you normally wear a suit, wear casual slacks and a sweater. Wear a heavy necklace that will jog your memory every time you move. Or experiment by wearing a rubber band around your wrist. Snap it every few minutes to remind yourself of who you are and where you're going.

Better still, program your mind-computer through guided imagery (see chapter 11) to self-remember every fifteen minutes throughout the day.

As your new beliefs become second nature, you will find yourself becoming less and less dependent on self-remembering. But during the first days or weeks, much of your success depends on remembering to stay in your newly chosen state of mind.

The key to self-remembering is this one simple fact: you are totally and completely free to choose your response to any stressful stimulus. You are free to respond to a stressful event with a positive thought rather than a negative thought. And you are totally free to transform a primitive expectation into a rather-belief.

Don't forget that you need transform only *primitive* expectations—that is, expectations based on primitive instincts that trigger the primitive fight-or-flight response (ego-power, seeking security through money and possessions, and so forth).

Programming out negative thoughts and emotions does not mean that you repress negative feelings. You are simply replacing negative thoughts with positive ones.

You may not be able to turn your mindset around 180 degrees and make life, and your health, into a total success immediately. But day by day, you clearly and definitely can program out all those damaging thoughts and expectations that are destroying your health and preventing you from becoming a disease-resistant Type B personality.

How to Reprogram Your Most Common Primitive Expectations

To help eliminate almost all primitive expectations, consider transforming the following common expectations into rather-beliefs. Use the rather-belief affirmations at the end of each example to overlay and replace the undesirable expectations. In a comparatively short time the rather-belief will take the place of the expectation in the very process of everyday living.

Comparing and competing. These practices create potentially destructive primitive expectations that, if unfulfilled, invariably arouse envy. Dr. Malcolm Carruthers, a clinical pathologist at St. Mary's Hospital in London, discovered that comparing yourself with friends and neighbors and trying to outdo them is a common source of stress. He found that people who live by the consumer creed, expecting more and more money and possessions, become highly vulnerable to stress and heart disease. Dr. Carruthers advises his patients to make their lives simple and uncomplicated and to stop seeking ego-power by competing with others, struggling for prominence, and acquiring possessions endlessly.

Envy is actually fear that you won't receive what your friends and neighbors are receiving. Envy and jealousy can keep your fight-or-flight response turned on indefinitely. They can kill you.

You can switch off envy by realizing that what you don't experience personally does not affect you. A newspaper report about tornado damage in a Cornbelt state may seem scary, but it won't affect you personally unless you experience it. Likewise, if your neighbor makes a million dollars, it won't affect you because you won't experience it.

Rather-belief: "I will not compete unnecessarily. I would rather cooperate instead of competing. I will not expect to become number one. I will not compare my achievements, possessions, losses, or failures with those of others. What I don't experience will not affect me."

Criticism.   We often criticize in an attempt to change another person's behavior because it does not conform to our expectations of how they should behave. However, criticism usually turns people off and makes them hostile.

Rather-belief: "I will avoid criticizing or putting down others. Instead, I would rather accept others as they are, be tolerant of their faults, and say things that will make them feel good."

Acting for rewards.   "Seek not the fruits of your actions" is an ancient yoga aphorism that warns us not to expect a reward for every act we do. If you devote a weekend to volunteer work, don't do it in the expectation that you are building up karma credit through which you will be repaid in the cosmic future. Work for love of the cause itself. If you help a neighbor, do it without any expectation that your neighbor is obligated to help you in return. Do things for the love of them, not to seek power or fame. Don't expect praise or reward for how well you do your job.

Rather-belief: "I would rather good things came my way. But instead of expecting a reward for my actions, I will congratulate myself for a job well done."

Injustice and unfairness.   Much emotional stress is caused by our primitive expectation that we should always receive what is due us and that whatever prevents its happening is unjust and unfair. An everyday example: Mrs. Smith volunteers to work long hours preparing for a church rummage sale. After the sale, the minister thanks Mrs. Jones (who put in only a few hours) for the sale's success and fails to mention Mrs. Smith at all. It seems unjust and unfair. (It also confirms the previous advice, "Seek not the fruits of your actions.") But injustice and unfairness are an everyday fact of life. Every year millions of Americans buy a car that turns out to be a lemon. They feel frustrated and believe it was unjust and unfair. This arouses negative emotions that cause the fight-or-flight state to simmer and that eventually make them sick.

Naturally, if you are deliberately swindled or ripped off, you should complain, but in a calm and loving way. If you're still being given unfair treatment, that may be the time to choose to become angry. If you decide that anger is appropriate, release the anger immediately.

54

We all would rather we always got what was due us. But you'll save a lot of emotional wear and tear if you simply stop expecting to be treated with justice and fairness.

Rather-belief: "I accept injustice and unfairness as a part of reality. I would rather get everything that is due me, but I don't expect to get it. Thus if I don't always get what seems due me, I shall not become angry or upset."

Judging what is right or wrong. You can eliminate a tremendous amount of stress by giving up being right. We must use our belief system to judge whether we or someone else is right or wrong. Our ego delights in drawing on past and outdated experiences, values, and folklore in our belief system to justify how right we are. Slip a thought into your mind about how you've been wronged, and you'll be bombarded by hours of mind-chatter telling you how unjust and unfair it all was and that you were actually right all the time.

Some people seem to spend their entire lives crusading to prove how right they were. By proving that some past event or act they did was right, they usually end up blaming someone else for being wrong. Because their fight-or-flight response is turned on all the time, expecting to be always right becomes an enormous drain on their energy.

What we so often fail to realize is that being right or wrong is totally unimportant. It just doesn't matter. What does count is how successfully your life works. If you can make your life work successfully through being wrong, then be wrong.

For example, I was flying back from Europe after a bicycle tour with an unboxed ten-speed. At the airport counter, the clerk said, "Sorry, we can't accept a bicycle unless it is boxed or bagged."

I said, "You're absolutely right. But I wonder if you could help me out. I'm booked on your Flight 35 which is leaving for Chicago in ninety minutes. I can't leave the bicycle here. If you could accept it, I'll sign a waiver releasing the airline of all responsibility."

The clerk not only accepted the bike but tagged it right through to Denver where it was delivered to my door the following morning without a scratch. Had I insisted on being right, the bike would never have left Europe. But by admitting I was wrong, I got what I wanted without incurring any worry or other negative emotion.

Rather-belief: "Since I would rather be calm, happy, and stress-free, I totally and completely, from this moment on, give up being right. I give up judging whether others are right or wrong. I also accept total responsibility for everything I think, feel, say, or do. Therefore, I cannot blame anyone else for anything I think, feel, say, or do."

"Past-ing." Recalling past events places images from the past on our inner movie screen. These images trigger emotions exactly as does the image of a thought we choose here and now. If you recall the death of a parent or spouse, you will experience sadness and stress, as you did when the death actually happened. Whenever you recall a stressful event from the past, you will experience the same negative emotions and a recurrence of the original stress.

People who feel they were wronged in the past or who bear resentment frequently recall the disturbing event. Each time they do, they experience the same emotional stress. The body goes into the fight-or-flight state and remains there until the "past-ing" stops.

Blaming oneself for past mistakes can also take a terrible toll in time, energy, and emotional stress. People who spend a lot of time and energy recalling disturbing events are often compelled to do so by their ego, which seeks through endless mind-chatter to prove that they were right after all and someone else was wrong.

In any case, the past is dead. We can't change it. Instead of focusing on a loved one's death, you can remember the good times you had with that person. If you feel that you took unfair advantage of someone in the past or that you would rather have treated someone better than you did, consider sending a personal note or a small gift as compensation.

Rather-belief: "If I must recall the past, I'd rather think only of the successes and good times. To be happy and content, I will allow neither the past nor the future to dominate my thoughts. All that really matters is to experience the moment here and now."

Trying to please everyone. One of the most disastrous primitive expectations (one that often triggers cancer) is that we expect love, respect, and approval from everyone for virtually everything we do.

First, you can't please everyone. Second, you're bound to win the disapproval of some people. Third, people who feel a need for the approval of everyone often become dependent on the approval of others. Often this dependency takes the form of asking all one's friends for advice before making a choice. This is another convenient cop-out by which we can duck the responsibility of making the choice ourselves. If our friends advise us to take choice A and choice A turns out to be a disaster, we can then blame our friends.

Rather-belief: "I'd rather everyone approved of me but since this is not possible, I will not expect, count on, or need the love and approval of others. While helping others is important, it doesn't mean I have to be a doormat and please everyone. What really counts is doing what I want to do in life, not doing what someone else thinks I should do in order to win love and approval. I also accept full and complete responsibility for every choice and decision I make and I will blame no one else for what happens."

Seeking ego-power, prestige, and fame.   Few of us like to admit it but we often spend a tremendous amount of time and energy acting out the belief that happiness can be ours if only we can get people and things to conform to our primitive expectations of how they should be. To achieve this end, we need ego-power to manipulate and control the people and things around us. Ego-power is ours in the form of money, occupational status and prestige, education, fame, possessions, wealth, and such false fronts as a luxury car, a fashionable address, or membership in an exclusive club. Trying to impress others with this sort of power is an energy-sapping game that can keep us permanently trapped in a low-level fight-or-flight state.

Rather-belief: "Though I would rather become eminent in my chosen occupation, I will not seek fame, power, status, prestige, or other pretensions of self-importance through my occupation or the amount of money I earn. Nor will I use my money or influence to manipulate people and things around me. Instead of expecting to change the world, I will change myself so that I accept the world as it is and flow along in harmony with it."

Security and survival.   We all should assume responsibility for our own security. The trouble is that we tend to react with the same me-versus-them attitude that our early ancestors had to use to survive in their primitive environment. Nowadays this same conditioning magnifies such minor risks as a letter from the IRS into an awesome threat to our survival.

Of course, absolute security doesn't exist. Millions of dollars in the world's safest bank could be reduced to worthless paper overnight by the ravages of inflation. The nation could be invaded or taken over by armed terrorists and your home and belongings taken away from you and nationalized. The Social Security system could break down. There just isn't any such thing as permanent and absolute security.

The closest thing to genuine security is being in the win-power state of mind all of the time. Being in the win-power state will allow you to rise above any adversity. You should also make high-level wellness a priority in your life. With win-power plus robust health we become resourceful creatures able to adapt successfully to almost any life change.

As a formula, the closest thing to security might be written:

Win-Power + High-Level Wellness + Adaptability + Resoucefulness + Know-how + Positive Thinking = Security.

Rather-belief: "I would rather have financial security, but since security doesn't exist, there is also no such state as insecurity. My security will come from the win-power state and good health."

5. New-Beliefs That Make You Well

FOR YEARS Rose Wilbur, a forty-five-year-old woman, had been diagnosed as having high blood pressure and had been taking antihypertensive medication. The side effects of the medication constantly made her feel unwell. Her job in an advertising agency caused her to always feel tense and her only relief was the pleasure of eating. Consequently, Rose was twenty pounds overweight. She smoked a pack of cigarettes a day and strictly avoided exercise.

Rose's father had been a physician and Rose had grown up to regard any form of nonmedical treatment as quackery. Her own doctor had told her that hypertension was incurable and had never mentioned the possibility of any alternative therapy. Rose believed that her high blood pressure was something that just happened. She considered it completely beyond her control, an attitude that made her feel quite helpless. Rose had no goals, future hopes, or aspirations, and saw little to go on living for.

One day she picked up a copy of a well-known nutrition magazine and read about a drugless program that had reversed hypertension in 85 percent of patients, using only exercise and diet. During an eighteen-month period beginning in 1976 at the Longevity Research Center in California, a total of 218 confirmed hypertensives, all on antihypertensive medication, were given a twenty-six-day lifestyle rehabilitation program. Rose read that under medical supervision each patient had commenced a progressive daily walking program coupled with a diet that virtually excluded all fat, salt, caffeine, refined carbohydrates, and excessive animal protein. At discharge, 186 of the 218 patients no longer needed antihypertensive medication.

Rose was amazed. If these results were true, why hadn't her doctor told her that it was possible to reverse hypertension without continuing to take the debilitating drugs?

Suddenly Rose experienced a feeling of lightness and freedom, of limitless new dimensions that gave her a multiplicity of choices and alternatives. She realized that, rather than being made a helpless invalid by her drugs, she herself had the power to go on being sick or to change her life and become well. Rose understood that by having grown up to regard medical science as infallible, she had regarded her doctor as an authority figure. But she discovered that she need no longer be a prisoner of her own outdated beliefs. Suddenly the magazine article had given her an entirely new perspective on life. Now, instead of drugs there was hope!

Rose realized that, as long as she was willing to face the consequences, she was perfectly free to stop taking her unpleasant medication. No one was forcing her to take it. Rose was an intelligent woman; she did not stop taking her medication immediately. She asked around until she learned of a doctor who specialized in preventive medicine. He ordered her to stop smoking at once, to reduce her weight, and to begin a daily walking program. Meanwhile he signed her up for a four-week program at a cardiac rehabilitation center.

Rose was so elated with her newfound power that she chose to stop smoking, cold turkey. She quit her job and spent four weeks at the rehabilitation center learning how she was to live for the rest of her life. After two weeks the doctor at the center took her off all antihypertensive medication. By the twenty-eighth day Rose's weight was back to normal, she was walking eight miles a day, she was enthusiastic about her new low-fat diet, and her blood pressure was back to normal. She was lean and athletic and had never felt better.

What was so significant about Rose's transformation from an overmedicated, helpless Type C personality to a radiant, well-adjusted Type B?

First, of course, as Rose herself discovered, drugs do not cure hypertension. High blood pressure is merely a symptom of an abnormal imbalance of the glandular and hormone output, caused in Rose's case by the way her outdated belief system interpreted stressful life situations as threatening and harmful. When Rose underwent the rehabilitation program, the holistic treatment was directed at reversing the *cause* of her high blood pressure and not at merely alleviating symptoms.

Yet behind even this was the sudden mental transformation she had experienced, the realization that the power to change her life and health was in her own hands and not in the hands of her doctor.

Mindshift: The Power to Change Your Life and Health

Rose saw that her life was being run by inappropriate and outdated beliefs from her past. Her belief that only drugs could treat hypertension had ruined her life and made her an invalid for years. In a sudden flash of realization, her mind turned completely around and refused to be run any longer by primitive programming. It is a condition that psychologists call mindshift, meaning a transition to a higher level of consciousness. The Shakers sought this same mindshift and described it as the ability to "turn, turn, turn."

Mindshift often comes suddenly, like learning to swim or ride a bicycle. All at once you discover you are using your mind in a totally new way. You become aware of the dangers of being programmed by outdated beliefs. Your mind turns away from the primitive beliefs that have made you sick and is ready to be programmed by enlightened new-beliefs that can make you well.

Mindshift also puts you in control of your life. Most people are not in charge of their lives. They simply react to everything around them.

"If I get a raise, I'll vacation in Europe."

"If I lose my present job, I'll train for a new and more satisfying career."

"If my cholesterol level is high, I'll begin an exercise program."

By contrast, once you have turned your mind around and are in the driver's seat, life becomes a continuous process of making decisions designed to improve your health, happiness, and quality of life.

No longer will your life be run by ifs, buts, or doubts. Once your mind is turned around, it is within your power to choose to be or to do anything you want. You have the freedom and power to choose to go to Europe, to train for a new career, or to begin an exercise program regardless of whether we are in the midst of depression, inflation, strikes, hurricanes, or an international crisis.

While you may still choose not to do these things, you now have the freedom and power to choose to do them if you wish. You are no longer locked in by mindset, by narrow, confining, outdated beliefs that prevent you from choosing what you want to do or become.

Once you are in charge of your life you have the power to think autonomously. You have the power to choose a positive thought in response to any stressful life event. You can choose to build a system of enlightened new-beliefs that will interpret most life events as free of stress. You may also choose to keep all your existing beliefs that you find beneficial.

You can choose a new life, new goals, new purpose, new health, and new directions. No longer are you dependent on external events or situations. You have become a self-starter. Now you are a person who *causes* things to happen.

How to Achieve Mindshift

"Most people are run by their outdated beliefs and believe they cannot change them," Norman Vincent Peale has said. The famous positive thinker adds that "you can change your life by changing your mental attitude. It's a marvelous fact that nobody needs to remain as he or she is."

As Peale and every other pioneer of inner healing has discovered, mindshift occurs when a realization that our health and our lives have been harmed by primitive beliefs leads us to begin acquiring health-building new-beliefs that can turn our health and our lives around.

Chapter 4 described how we can render our primitive expectations harmless by transforming them into rather-beliefs. In this chapter you will learn about the benefits of health-restoring new-beliefs that everyone can acquire. As you begin to program out your primitive beliefs and replace them with new-beliefs, mindshift will naturally occur.

You'll very probably experience mindshift as the traditional "Aha!" experience. In Zen, est, and other disciplines where the truth suddenly dawns on people as understanding emerges, the immediate reaction is to exclaim "Aha!" However, not everyone attains mindshift all at once: the transition may be gradual or it may occur step by step. However you "get it," the experience is like being reborn.

As mindshift occurs, it will reinforce the changeover that you have already begun to make by programming out primitive beliefs and programming in health-restoring new-beliefs.

Here, then, are the most common beneficial new-beliefs. Make them a part of your attitude and philosophy as quickly as possible. Use the affirmations to help your mind-computer accept these beliefs. They will quickly become a permanent part of your personality through the very process of life itself.

How to Accept the Most Common New-Beliefs

One requirement for accepting any new-belief is your total willingness to take full responsibility for everything that comes into your life as a result. Regardless of what happens, there is no one to blame for anything, no one is right or wrong, and you definitely refrain from criticizing, comparing, or evaluating other people's motives.

Ideally, you should plan your inner work around accepting one of these new-beliefs each day. Use the self-remembering technique to keep reminding yourself about each new-belief you are accepting. You can easily recall the key word of each new-belief by memorizing this sentence: *Accept changes* on *faith* by *giving* this *moment* an *abundance* of *open relationships* that *work.*

Abundance. A widespread belief we'd all be better off without is "I could be happy if only I had more things and more money."

How true is it? For most of us the problem is not that we need more. It's that we'd probably be better off with less. Virtually all middle-class Americans would be healthier and probably happier if they had fewer possessions to keep maintaining, to find spare parts for, to worry about losing, or to become enslaved by. The plain truth is that almost every one of us is rich right now. We're already blessed with an abundance of life's necessities. You already have right now everything you need to make you happy.

An ancient Hindu proverb puts it more succinctly: "Live unknown. Make your wants few."

New-belief: "I believe the world is a friendly, beautiful place and that it has already given me everything I need to be happy. I believe I can become even happier by simplifying my life, making it less complicated, and making my wants fewer. No amount of money or things can buy good health or satisfying relationships. As long as I have an abundance of both, I am richer than any millionaire."

Acceptance. Accept the world as it is. Accept people the way they are, including their dedication to being right and their outdated beliefs. (After all, you do not have to believe in their beliefs.) Accept events and situations that you cannot change and be content with things the way they are. Accept everything that was previously unacceptable to your primitive beliefs.

Most people see the world as they believe it should be, not as it is. To try to live out their primitive expectations in this make-believe world is an energy-sapping game. The result is constant and unavoidable stress.

This doesn't mean, of course, that you should not attempt to improve things that are within your power to improve. But these improvements should always be carried out in a spirit of love and calm. If it seems you must upset yourself emotionally to change something, use techniques #2, #3, and #4, along with transforming primitive expectations into rather-beliefs to cancel out the stress and prevent negative emotions.

New-belief: "I believe in accepting life, the world, and everyone in it as they are. Instead of trying to change the world I will change my own programming so that I harmonize and flow with life instead of trying to fight it. While I am not going to be a doormat or a helpless Type C personality, neither am I going to destroy myself through emotional stress as a result of trying to change things that are beyond my control."

Changes. Stress is caused by our having to adjust to changes created by obstacles, setbacks, crises, difficulties, and other (not necessarily negative) life events. Changes, however, do not have to be interpreted as stressful. Without some changes life would be dull and monotonous.

63

Technique #3 will help you transform stressful expectations into stress-free rather-beliefs and the other inner healing techniques in this book can help you learn to remove the stress from any life event.

Since the majority of people have not learned to successfully cancel out stress, they continue to believe that obstacles and setbacks should be feared and avoided. But for those who are confident of their ability to deal with stress, this is another outdated belief. Instead, we should welcome setbacks and obstacles. Why? Each fresh problem may provoke and reveal the existence of yet another unsuspected primitive expectation that we have not yet transformed into a rather-belief. Only by welcoming fresh obstacles as learning experiences can we gradually detect our remaining primitive expectations. And only by programming out these lingering old beliefs can we grow.

New-belief: "I believe that only by welcoming obstacles, setbacks, and other life changes can I discover all the hidden primitive expectations that could make me sick. Thus, I welcome changes, obstacles, and problems as learning experiences to help me grow. Every person about whom I can still get upset provides another potential growth experience. Instead of interpreting changes as stressful, I believe that changes are interesting and stimulating adventures."

Faith.   Certainly in a crime-ridden country like America, there is some justification for not trusting strangers. Yet this belief is often overinterpreted in our mind-computers to produce a similar but erroneous belief that all strangers should be regarded with suspicion and distrust. This belief makes us suspicious, intolerant, fearful, and eventually sick. Surveys have shown that people who trust strangers are healthier, happier, and better adjusted. By "strangers" I mean people with whom you are not familiar. They may be your next-door neighbors. I am not suggesting that you invite into your home unknown people who might possibly be dangerous.

It is a fact that most people respond to us the same way we treat them. Thus, we should treat all strangers lovingly and regard them as honest and trustworthy until they prove otherwise. This does not mean indiscriminately trusting strangers with confidences or material goods, but it means being open and loving with everyone you meet.

New-belief: "I believe that most people have good motives and are eager to help rather than hurt. Therefore, I shall treat all strangers lovingly and assume they are honest until they prove otherwise."

Giving, helping.   The belief that we should give to and help others is a key factor in leading a long and healthful life. Yet all too many people still believe only in getting and receiving. If we all share our time and effort in a spirit of love, all of humanity becomes one. We are all really giving and receiving, without regard for obligation and expectation.

Our giving and receiving does not have to involve money. The greatest gift you can give some people is to sit down and listen to them; let them tell you about their problems. In return you can suggest possible solutions. One of the most loving acts is to spend some time each week visiting an elderly shut-in or someone in a hospital. Or call somebody long-distance or visit a neighbor. Being loving, warm, and generous is typical of Type B personalities.

New-belief: "I believe that giving and helping spontaneously without thought of reward are essential to high-level wellness. I believe that only a person who is in charge of his or her life can enjoy helping others. Conversely, I believe that only through giving freely and helping others can I achieve complete control of my life."

The moment. Almost all negative emotions are evoked by thoughts about the past or future. But we cannot experience the past or the future; we can experience only the present moment. The here and now is all we've got. Yet most people still believe that their happiness lies someplace in the future. When the kids leave home or when our Social Security begins or when we retire or when our vacation starts, suddenly everything will become perfect and happiness will be ours.

Not so! We can't experience happiness tomorrow or next year. We can feel happy only here and now.

This is not to imply that you should drop all concern for the future, stop recalling past pleasures, or stop planning for future goals. Yet most of us are so conditioned to future-ing or past-ing that when we direct our awareness to the moment, our minds are flooded with chatter reminding us about yesterday's or tomorrow's problems. It is still a fact that almost all our emotional stress arises from thinking about the future or past. Programming ourselves to believe that what is important in life is here and now can eliminate 90 percent of our stressful thoughts.

The way to do it is to tune in to your sensory input. Sharpen your appreciation of everything that is going on around you. Become deeply absorbed in enjoying and experiencing everything you say, do, hear, feel, see, smell, taste, or touch. Stop structuring and scheduling all your time. Take time to become deeply aware of everything going on around you: birds singing, trees, flowers, a sunset, colors, patterns of light and shade, the sky and stars, sunshine, rain, frost, or snow. Direct your awareness to the now. Discover pleasure in the people you are with, in simple activities like walking or talking.

People who have been near death and have recovered treasure each moment of the day. But you don't have to almost lose your life to begin appreciating it.

New-belief: "I believe that right now is all I have. I believe in living it for all it's worth. I believe I have everything I need to be happy right now. The past has gone and the future has not arrived. I believe I can only experience life here and now. Therefore, I will continue to enjoy the present, moment by moment, throughout the day. I will loosen up and devote myself to enjoying the now all of the time. I will live a simpler, less structured life, and I will do fun things spontaneously. I believe the purpose of life is to enjoy it. And I can only enjoy it right now!"

Being open and truthful. The widely held belief that we should be reserved and keep our real feelings private, or that it's all right not to be completely truthful, is a major cause of negative emotions. Failing to share your innermost feelings separates you from other people. It also means you must repress and hide negative emotions. Being untruthful prevents us from knowing our real selves. And it creates constant stress as we continually strive to remember the lies we have told various people and to keep on telling more untruths to support those we have already told.

Failing to be completely open and truthful means we are continually hiding our real feelings through pretenses and game playing. All this invokes a helpless feeling that defines us as Type C personalities.

Two recent studies show that being open and outgoing leads to inner joy and also strengthens the immune system, which protects us from infections and cancer. The common cold research unit of Harvard Hospital in England made a study of fifty-two people, dividing them into introverts and extroverts. Each person was given a cold virus. Results showed that the introverts tended to get more and worse colds than the extroverts. Another study at the University of California revealed that frank, open people are much happier than people who keep their feelings closed and hidden.

Being open means making your inner self transparent to everyone. You conceal nothing. You hold back no part of you. You have no secrets. You are always completely frank, authentic, honest, and truthful. Except where telling the exact truth may cause harm or suffering (a rare occurrence), you tell the truth completely at all times. You automatically stop playing games, acting out roles, and living behind a mask of pretenses.

As you open yourself completely, you will discover that others are also willing to share their deepest secrets and innermost feelings. Suddenly you see the world as a friendly, happy, hospitable place and all stress disappears.

Being open does not mean you need to give up privacy. It only means giving up being private.

New-belief: "I believe in being completely open and transparent. I believe in sharing my inner self and my innermost secrets and feelings. I believe in telling the exact truth at all times and in being completely honest in all my dealings. Henceforth, my word is my bond."

Relationships. Another health-destroying belief is the concept that it's all right to be aloof and impersonal, to live alone, and to avoid intimate contact with others. These forms of nonrelationships may be convenient, but they are definitely not good for our health.

A sixteen-year study of the medical and social history of the small Italian-American town of Roseto, Pennsylvania, revealed that people who are members of extended, close-knit families have 50 percent fewer heart attacks than the general population. University scientists examined every detail in the lives of the people in Roseto, including diet and exercise, and they found that the only significant difference between them and the general population was the close-knit ties resulting from Roseto's traditional multigeneration families.

Another study based on over 100,000 questionnaires prepared and analyzed by Dr. Jonathon L. Freedman, a professor of psychology at Columbia University, concluded that married people were happiest. Sixty-eight percent of married people reported they were happy, and 54 percent of singles reported being happy. Topping the happiness scale were married couples followed by couples living together, single men over thirty-five, single women under thirty-five, single men under thirty-five, and single women over thirty-five. Least happy were divorced men and women and widows and widowers who had not remarried.

Other studies show that men and women with strong personal ties and relationships at home, at work, at church, and in their community are significantly more resistant to stress. Still other studies have shown that touching and hugging lower blood pressure, decrease the pulse rate, and cause the hypothalamus to switch on the calm state. Yet other studies have demonstrated that friends and family are vital to high-level wellness.

What all these studies are saying is that human contact makes us feel good, needed, and loved. Only through friends and family can we find the therapy of touch, contact, and emotional nourishment. Everyone needs a strong, supportive network of relatives and friends.

Yet millions of people continue to believe they should measure and judge the success of their lives in material terms like money and acquisitions. This is a self-defeating primitive belief. Instead of collecting money and possessions, we should collect satisfying relationships. Good health is impossible without social ties and social support. Moreover, touching and hugging, preferably skin to skin, is a basic human need. High blood pressure and tension can often be relieved merely by soothing and rubbing a person's neck, arms, and shoulders.

Most people in need of human contact are Type C personalities. Many feel so helpless they are unwilling to risk marriage. Others are so withdrawn they have no friends. Through the very act of dumping their old beliefs and becoming willing to risk new friendships and even marriage, such people can transform themselves from disease-prone Type C's into disease-resistant Type B personalities.

Meeting people and making new relationships isn't difficult. To multiply your contacts with others, simply get out and join a church or a square dance group. Sign up for adult education classes, exercise classes, a bridge club, or an outdoor recreation club. Once you meet people, listen to what they say. Be patient and don't interrupt. Stay tuned in and responsive. Keep eye contact. Forget your own interests and problems and concentrate on those of others. Avoid criticizing, complaining, judging, or arguing. Among a group, move around and talk with people who have different interests. Give everyone a real hug if you can. Try to touch and be touched on every occasion.

Use every opportunity to broaden your circle of friends. Carry a notebook and note the name, address, phone number, and interests of every person you meet. Visit people and spend time talking. Instead of buying an expensive gift, visit someone and let that person talk to you.

Another primitive belief that everyone should drop immediately is that it is desirable to depend on friends for loans of money or other valuable items. In fact, we should never depend on friends or relatives for things, like money, that we should provide ourselves. Depending on friends and relatives, including parents, for things we should provide ourselves is just another way of avoiding responsibility for our own lives.

Many people believe that being alone is a terrifying, anxious, depressing experience that inevitably makes life seem empty. We experience these negative emotions because that is what we believe. If you must be alone at times, slide aside any thoughts of fear or anxiety and replace them with a thought that, far from being a catastrophe, being alone can be comfortable and peaceful. Being alone and feeling lonely are two very different experiences.

If you fear loneliness, focus on your loneliness and experience it. Slide a thought onto your inner movie screen that no one is bothering you right now and that being alone is restful and peaceful. Realize that feeling lonely is simply the way your mind-computer has been programmed to interpret being alone. You feel melancholy because of an expectation that you should always be surrounded by supportive people. And that expectation is not being fulfilled.

68

New-belief: "Although I would rather be among friends, I am not going to let being alone upset me. I realize that loneliness is really a form of boredom. So I am going to become absorbed in some activity I enjoy. I also realize that many people actually enjoy solitude and being alone. So I'll go for a long walk or ride a bicycle and enjoy the silence and peace. As I read, write, paint, walk, bicycle, or do something else that I really enjoy, my boredom and loneliness will vanish. I believe in expanding my range of social contacts. I believe that high-level wellness cannot be attained without human contact, especially through loving, caring, hugging, touching, talking, and listening to others. I believe in multiplying my contacts to include people of all ages from children to older people. I believe I would be happier if married (or living with someone else), and if the opportunity comes I will accept the risk and go ahead. I believe that I should not depend on friends for things I should provide myself. Finally, I believe I should accept all people the way they are."

Work. One of the most unhealthy beliefs in our society is that we should continue to do work that we dislike in order to remain safe and secure. Numerous studies have shown that the most common single source of stress and subsequent ill health is job dissatisfaction.

Satisfying work should be a source of stimulation and pleasure. Work that we enjoy, that makes the maximum use of our talents, and in which we take pride leaves few, if any, stress scars. Stressful jobs can be high-pressure jobs requiring a large amount of responsibility or those involving dull, repetitive work. Whatever the work, the largest single cause of job-related emotional stress is continuing to do something you dislike. Underneath that stress is the outdated belief that we should stick with the safe and familiar and not take risks by striking out for something new and unknown. Job stress can be eliminated by achieving mindshift and by accepting the belief that you have the power to change your life and to start doing work that you really enjoy.

It would be irresponsible to give up your job right away. But if you continue to work at a meaningless occupation, you are not really in charge of your life. If you must continue to work at an unsatisfactory job or if you need some time to focus on your job-related goals, the techniques in this book can help reduce the stress of your present job.

Stop and ask yourself what is really important in your life. Acquiring material possessions? Or living a satisfying life based on personal relationships and fulfillment? Being dependent on other people and on outside situations and events? Or being in charge of your life? How can your job relate to what is most important to you? How can your job help you achieve what is most important?

New-belief: "I believe that to enjoy high-level wellness, I should do work that I enjoy. If I am thirty years old, I have approximately 14,000 days left (including weekends) in which to work. I will be on this earth only once. Work that I dislike is a major cause of stress, and statistics show that it leads to sickness. I believe that I can eliminate the stress by using inner healing techniques. I also believe that I am fully responsible to family members who are dependent on me and that I should not jeopardize their welfare by taking unnecessary risks. Nor should I do anything that would make me a burden on the community or on others. Within this framework, I do believe that I have the power to choose to do the kind of work I enjoy doing. I will accept this belief into my personal programming. I believe that, consciously and subliminally, it will motivate my mind-computer to find a way through which I can spend the rest of my life doing satisfying work that I really enjoy."

This has been a review of only the most basic new-beliefs that many people find beneficial. You can probably think of other new-beliefs that you personally can integrate into your life.

6. Total Wellness through Love and Joy

A SIX-YEAR STUDY by the American Institutes for Research concluded that the key ingredient for happiness among men and women of all ages is good health.

Happiness is health. You can't be healthy unless you're happy. People who are happy and joyful all the time are in a continuous state of high-level wellness. That's because joy is a positive emotion and, like all positive emotions, it triggers the hypothalamus to turn on the calm state. Happy people feel peaceful and relaxed and live in a state of ease in which their whole person thrives.

Happiness is not something that will come to you by sitting around and waiting. Nor can it be bought or even sought. Lasting happiness can be experienced only as a by-product of a satisfying activity that involves such new-belief qualities as loving, caring, sharing, being concerned, giving freely, and helping others. Joy and happiness, like all emotions, are preceded by thoughts that come from such satisfying activities.

Happy people are programmed by new-beliefs that place value on qualities such as accepting life the way it is, being generous, being open, and loving everyone without reservation. Lasting happiness cannot be attained through seeking more money or acquiring more possessions. Unhappy people are programmed by primitive beliefs that tell them the way to be happy is to pursue primitive needs, wants, desires, and expectations. When their primitive expectations go unmet, they feel upset and they try to change and manipulate the world outside to make it conform to their expectations. When the world still does not conform, they experience stress.

The plain truth is that the traditional ways in which we were taught to seek happiness just don't work. Despite this, two thirds of the human race—virtually all Type A's and C's—continue to seek happiness through fulfilling ambitions and working more efficiently to get more money and material

71

goods. As their desires for money, things, skills, ego-power, status, prestige, and security fail to work out as they expected, their inner peace and calm is steadily eroded.

But almost everyone with a Type A or C personality was taught from infancy to depend for happiness on people, events, and things outside themselves. They have been conditioned to believe they are not responsible for or in control of their own feelings. Yet in reality it is not outside events that make us feel good or bad. It is what we believe about an event or about what a person says that evokes a negative feeling. If you believe that something a person says is insulting, you will feel angry. If you believe you have been treated unjustly, you will feel resentful. If you believe that something a person said is hurtful, you will feel hurt.

How can we enjoy happiness all of the time? By realizing that happiness comes from within. We feel happy when our mind-computer chooses a productive and joyful thought.

As you attain mindshift and replace outdated beliefs with healthful new-beliefs, you will automatically become a happier person. As you accept new-beliefs into your belief system, your mind-computer will begin to choose only effective and positive thoughts. Regardless of how stressful the stimuli are, your new belief system will refuse to choose a negative thought and will produce only positive, loving, and joyful thoughts.

Does this mean you can be joyful and happy all of the time? The answer is an unqualified yes. Except for obvious times when grief and sadness are appropriate, such as when mourning someone's death or when sympathizing with someone's misfortune, you *can* be happy all of the time. Through inner healing methods you can avoid all of the negative feelings that unhappy people experience. Instead, you need never drop below the mid-point on the happiness scale. And you can be free to soar to the heights of ecstasy.

We Can Feel Whatever We Choose to Feel

We must accept complete responsibility for all our feelings and we must realize that external events are not responsible for how we think, feel, or act. We react to stressful events the way our belief system has been programmed to react. It is the negative thoughts that we allow our belief system to choose that make us unhappy. We must cease blaming somebody or something outside us for the way we feel inside. External events may influence the thoughts our belief system chooses. But the choosing and the feeling take place inside our mind-computer.

The next step is to realize that we are totally and completely free to place in our mind any thought that we choose to place there. We are free to choose any thought in response to any outside stimulus. We don't have to put up with the thoughts our mind-computer chooses for us.

Since a thought must precede each emotion we feel, we ourselves can choose to feel any way we desire to feel by deliberately choosing an appropriate thought. If someone says something that our belief system might recognize as hurtful, we are perfectly free to respond by choosing a positive, cheerful thought. If someone says something that our belief system would normally recognize as insulting, we are perfectly free to respond with a loving thought and a feeling of love instead of a feeling of anger and hate.

If at any time your new-beliefs fail to interpret incoming data as stress-free, you can still continue to feel comfortable and unthreatened by choosing thoughts that make you feel good.

This chapter deals with emotions: how to eliminate upsetting negative emotions like resentment or fear and how to replace them with calming, positive emotions like love or joy. The following inner healing techniques flow naturally from one into the other. They are designed to help program out health-destroying negative emotions and replace them with health-building feelings.

INNER HEALING TECHNIQUE #4
How to Feel Whatever You Choose to Feel

Most of us have taught ourselves to react to whatever we believe is a stressful situation by choosing a negative emotion such as resentment or anger. Anything we have learned, however, can also be unlearned: we can learn to choose a calm and loving thought instead. Any one of us can feel any way we choose to feel right now. Since every feeling is preceded by a thought, all we need to do is choose a positive thought.

Most people try to change their feelings. It doesn't work. To change your feelings you must first change the thought that produced the feeling. Here's how it's done.

At the first hint of any thought that threatens to produce an upsetting feeling, boldly take the following steps immediately.

1. Pinch your wrist and call out, "Stop! Stop!" (Do this silently if other people are around.)

2. Swiftly slide aside the negative thought that is on your inner movie screen, leaving the screen blank.

3. Choose an appropriate but completely positive thought. Slide the image of this thought onto your inner movie screen. Hold it there. If other thoughts intrude, slide these aside and slide the positive thought back on.

What kind of thought should you choose? If you can't think of anything else, slide a thought-image of a beautiful garden or beach scene onto your inner movie screen (as described in technique #2). You can produce a feeling of happiness at any time by projecting an image of a happy event out of the past. Try to select an event that involved at least one new-belief. Perhaps last week, for example, you donated half a day to helping out at your local day care center or senior citizen center. You met and talked with a lot of warm, friendly, loving, evolved Type B people, and you felt good afterward because you had done something satisfying and worthwhile.

All of us have had experiences that produced lasting happiness. By re-creating the same thought-image produced by the experience and by holding that image in our mind we can experience the same joyful, happy feeling that we experienced in the past.

At any time we can stop oncoming fear, worry, anxiety, anger, hate, resentment, hurt, or any other negative emotion by sliding aside the thought that is about to produce it and by replacing it with an effective thought, that is, a thought that lets you flow along with life instead of trying to fight it. Many of the more enlightened and evolved Type B's are able to instantly choose a calming and loving response when a person is insulting or hostile. Almost anyone should be able to do the same after having undergone the mindshift transformation.

For example, Bill and Daphne Curtis, an older couple, rented out the cottage in back of their home to a younger couple. The younger couple agreed to water and cut the lawn around the cottage and to refrain from playing their stereo outdoors. During the summer the young couple became lax about watering and cutting the grass and one evening they held a party at which they played loud music on their stereo outdoors.

Bill, who had high blood pressure, felt his anger soar. But Daphne asked him: "Isn't that because you *expected* our tenants not to turn their stereo on loud? And that you *expected* them to care for the lawn? Now that your expectations are not working out, you feel angry and upset."

Bill agreed. He tensed each muscle group in his body one by one to work off the tension and release his anger. Then he quickly slid aside his image of the young couple as noisy and undependable. On his inner movie screen he now saw them as the warm, loving young couple who had come in every day to talk to him last winter when he had the flu. Within minutes Bill felt warm, loving, and happy again.

Then he transformed his primitive expectation into a rather-belief. "I would rather they cut the grass and were quieter. But I will not be upset if they don't meet my expectations. I accept them as they are and I love them without reservation. This is the first party they have had and we can easily drown out their stereo by turning on our own. Besides, I'm grateful that they did play their stereo loud. It proved to be a learning experience. It taught me I still had an expectation that needed reprogramming."

An hour later Bill took his own blood pressure and found it only slightly above normal.

At first you'll probably want to use the self-remembering method (technique #3) to remind yourself that you are now free to respond to a stimulus with any thought that you choose. You are free to choose either health or disease.

It is important to realize that when you practice technique #4, you are not repressing a feeling. You are preventing a negative feeling from materializing by replacing the negative seed-thought with a positive thought before it can evoke a negative emotion. Therefore, you do not experience a negative emotion at all.

How to Program Every Day into a Happy, Wonderful Day

Because only you can choose your own feelings, you are in total control of your own happiness. Any one of us can choose to program a completely happy, healthy day every day. You can choose in the evening that you will have a completely happy day the following day. Regardless of what happens in the outside world, you will have a wonderful day all day tomorrow if you so choose.

A few simple behavioral steps can reinforce your intention to eliminate unhappiness. Immediately upon waking up, insert a joyful, loving seed-thought onto your inner movie screen. Smile, stretch, and remind yourself that you are going to have a relaxed, happy, and satisfying day. Get up right away and if possible go outside and greet the day. Extend your arms toward the sun. If you can, walk barefoot on grass. Take a few minutes to absorb, to feel, and to experience the presence of nature. If that isn't possible, admire a handsome building or a statue or a picture or an indoor plant. Then count your blessings and experience gratitude for everything you have. Remind yourself that you have everything you need to be happy right now. If you have health, love, and satisfying relationships, you are already richer than most millionaires.

As you return indoors, look at yourself in a mirror. Even if you are still a bit overweight, like and love the image you see. Declare with enthusiasm: "I am healthy and happy. I feel brimful of vigor and energy. All day today I shall love everyone without reservation. I shall accept life the way it is. I shall give and help freely. And I shall laugh and have fun. Life is just a fun game. I'm going to enjoy it to the hilt. I am the luckiest, richest person alive. I shall have a wonderfully satisfying and happy day."

You can minimize exposure to negative stimuli by preferring to mix as far as possible with positive, Type B people. Avoid negative people and those who constantly tell you how wrong you are. Pass up depressing news items on TV and in the newspaper.

Contrary to what most of us have been taught, we do not have to permit ourselves to become angry if something annoys us. Instead, through our new-belief system we no longer interpret external events as annoying.

But what if we momentarily forget and do allow our mind-computer to choose a negative thought? What if we do become angry, fearful, hurt, or upset? Then it's too late! You can choose a positive thought only when the mind is still relatively calm. Once you experience a destructive emotion, you must release it as quickly as possible by using technique #5. Only then, when mental calm is restored, can you return to using technique #4.

INNER HEALING TECHNIQUE #5
How to Release Negative Emotions Vigorously and Immediately

If and when a negative emotion does occur, release and express it completely just as soon as you can. People who get cancer, ulcers, or infectious diseases are invariably passive Type C personalities who turn numb and bottle up and hold in their negative emotions. So give your feelings full freedom just as soon as you can do so without harming anyone or looking foolish.

Negative emotions trigger the hypothalamus to turn on the fight-or-flight state, which puts the body into an alarm condition, tensed up for a physical battle or for flight. In primitive surroundings we would do either one or the other and no harm would result. But in civilized society, the very best way to release tension is either to run or jog or to punch and stomp on a substitute enemy. Any kind of vigorous exercise, including swimming, bicycling, digging, sawing, rowing, paddling, or brisk walking, is equally effective. If you cannot do this, use one of the muscle-tensing techniques described in chapter 8. Briefly, you tense the muscles in each limb of your body—one limb at a time—for about eight seconds, then release them. Tense and release first one leg, then the other leg, followed by your buttocks, abdomen, arms, chest and back muscles, neck, face, and scalp. Or, if you can, tense every muscle in the body simultaneously, hold for eight seconds, and release. Repeat three times. This will activate and release all muscular tension.

Here are other recommended cathartic exercises for eliminating a negative emotion and releasing pent-up tension.

1. Stomp around the yard, block, or park, imagining you are stomping your feet on the person you dislike.

2. Punch a bag, bean bag, pillow, or mattress while you imagine you are punching the person you dislike.

3. Roll up and twist a towel as you imagine you are twisting the arm of the person you dislike.

4. Hit golf balls as you imagine on each one the face of the person you dislike.

5. Let out your emotion by crying and sobbing. This is one of the best forms of catharsis, especially for men.

6. Achieve catharsis by laughing hysterically.

7. Yell with rage and hurt as you do any of the above things.

Combine at least one physical-release method with an emotional release like crying or yelling. It's completely therapeutic. Within minutes you'll experience a huge relief and release.

Once you've let out the tension and emotion, stop and take several deep breaths. Relax. Then mentally forgive the person who you believe is responsible for upsetting you. In your imagination, picture the person being showered with love, health, and abundance. Visualize yourself hugging and loving that person.

If you are prevented by social restraints from releasing your feelings, you can still tense and release each limb without anyone's noticing. Count backward from one hundred to zero while you picture each number on your inner movie screen. As soon as you are able, unleash any residual feelings with full force using one of the physical-release methods. Don't leave a trace of anger, fear, resentment, envy, or other negative emotion lingering in your system. Get it all out in the open.

To prevent a recurrence once you are calm again, confront the person who you believe caused the upset. Explain lovingly and gently what happened without embarrassing the other person. Look the other person straight in the eye all the time. Tell the other person that you feel hurt. Quite frequently the other person will apologize and will avoid provoking you in the future. If possible, end up by hugging the other person and feeling loving and caring toward him or her.

INNER HEALING TECHNIQUE #6
How to Get Rid of Repressed Emotions

A repressed emotion is almost invariably caused by a primitive expectation or belief deeply embedded in the subconscious mind. The emotion may have been repressed as long ago as early childhood. Almost every mental healing system agrees that a deeply buried belief can be reprogrammed only while a person is actually experiencing the hurt and pain caused by the repressed emotion. Recent experiments have shown, however, that the chief difficulty lies in actually identifying the existence of a repressed emotion together with the thought and belief that are causing it. Here is a simple and effective technique that identifies and eliminates the belief and the emotion.

Take six blank sheets of paper. Label each one at the top with a negative emotion: fear, worry, anxiety, anger, resentment, and envy. Over the next few days, as they occur to you, list on each sheet the names of people, things, or situations that produce each of the negative emotions. Keep the sheets available indefinitely. After you have listed the more obvious sources of emotional upset, others may gradually seep up through your subconscious and identify themselves.

Most orthodox books about psychology make it sound virtually impossible for any layperson to expose and identify repressed emotions that have been deeply buried for years. In practice, this is often not true. By making lists of the most obvious and immediate sources of repressed emotions, you will start your awareness probing for emotions that lie deeper in the subconscious. Slowly, subliminally, imperceptibly these deeply buried emotions will float to the surface. When one does, write down the details at once.

You yourself may be the most surprised person when an inner voice whispers, "I am jealous of Peter because he is a more successful real estate salesman than I am." Note down the reason why you are envious, or why you are angry, fearful, or resentful.

It's best to reprogram these stubborn cases by using guided imagery, which is described in chapter 11. But until you have learned that technique, you can do it quite effectively in the following way.

Lie or sit quietly and relax. Take a deep breath while you visualize the figure 10. Take another deep breath as you visualize the figure 9. Count slowly back to zero, holding each figure in your mind's eye as you take a deep breath.

Now visualize the person or thing that is arousing the negative emotion. Let's assume it is Peter, who sold two million dollars worth of real estate last year while you sold only one million. You weren't consciously aware of your envy. But as you visualize Peter, you feel a strong undercurrent of professional jealousy.

You realize that you also expected to sell two million dollars worth of property. But you didn't make it and Peter did. So you tell yourself, "I'd rather have hit the two-million-dollar mark but I'm not going to become upset because I didn't. Besides, Peter worked twice as hard as I did. He deserves it."

Keep repeating these phrases and visualizing Peter until you begin to experience the repressed envy. As the pain and hurt well up, keep repeating the phrases. Now visualize the phrases spelled out on your inner movie screen. Burn the phrases into your mind.

If you can, cry and sob and stomp your feet or beat your fists on the floor. All the while you are experiencing the repressed envy, keep visualizing Peter, his professional success, the homes he sold, the acclaim he received, and the money he made. Examine the pain and hurt you are experiencing. Tell yourself that being envious is not worthwhile. In a few minutes, possibly less, you will have released the repressed emotion and the pain and hurt will disappear.

As you calm down, keep repeating the mental process of transforming the primitive expectation into a rather-belief. Then visualize Peter again. Totally forgive him. Forgive yourself for being envious. In your imagination, picture Peter receiving love, health, and abundance. Visualize yourself hugging and loving him.

You must repeat this process for each thing or person on your lists. However, each session need occupy only twenty minutes, possibly less—a far better alternative to orthodox psychiatry, which often requires months of consultations at enormous expense.

The Dynamics of Negative Emotions

Fear is the basic motivation of all negative emotions. It underlies anger, hate, frustration, and resentment—the anger spectrum of emotions. It is also the basis of anxiety, worry, and envy—the fear spectrum of emotions.

You can actually eliminate most negative emotions if you can locate and analyze the fear that underlies them. To do so, ask yourself, "What am I afraid of?" If you are being upset by envy, for example, you may discover that the cause of your envy is actually fear that you will not receive something that the person you envy has received. As the answer comes to you, place your awareness on the fear and on the envy. The fear will usually vanish and along with it will go the envy.

To help you understand the dynamics of the negative emotions, I have analyzed each one and given proven methods for eliminating the emotion from your mind-computer. Use the rather-belief affirmations to help downgrade the expectations that are triggering your negative emotions.

Anxiety, worry, and fear. Anxiety and worry are different shades of fear. Anxiety is a vague uneasiness about a feared event. Worry is fear that a specific event may occur. Worry often concerns something we expect to get or something we have lost but expected to keep forever. Both anxiety and worry are caused by mind-chatter that emanates from fear.

Most worry arises from fear of loss, loneliness, pain, illness, poverty, dying, retiring, weight gain, inflation, accidents, losing a job, a depression, insecurity, becoming old, inability to meet bills and taxes, and getting cancer or heart disease. Other frequent worry sources concern the spouse, family, home, and car. Many of us are actually so conditioned to worrying that if there is nothing to worry about, our minds will seek out a new worry source. It usually isn't difficult. Newspapers and TV are filled with disturbing news, and advertising capitalizes on our fears of ill health and accidents to sell us everything from insurance to vitamins.

What we are anxious, worried, or fearful about is that we will be faced with some stressful change that will affect our comfort or lifestyle or that will effect a loss. As we worry about it we visualize it as real. We see it on our inner movie screen as though it had already happened. This thought-image reinforces our fear. The hypothalamus cannot distinguish between a real fear and an imagined one. Therefore it turns on the fight-or-flight response, creating glandular and hormonal imbalance.

Fear produces such distinctive symptoms as rapid pulse, nausea, digestive upset, dry mouth, tension, sweaty palms, and distress and uneasiness. As the sympathetic nervous system takes over, the blood lactate level rises, causing feedback that reinforces the original state of anxiety.

Action is the antidote to worry and other fear-spectrum emotions. If you're worried about your health, act and see a doctor right away. If you're worried about high blood pressure, act now to start losing weight and to stop smoking. If you're worried about approaching retirement, make bold plans for a successful retirement and begin carrying them out.

One centenarian, when asked how he had dealt with worry throughout his life, replied, "If I could do something about a problem, I would act. If there was nothing I could do, I would stop worrying about something that was beyond my power to change." Another technique used by this man was to ask himself, "Will what is worrying me make any difference to my life five years from now?" If the answer was no, he'd stop worrying about it.

Everybody is aware that being worried or anxious is a completely valueless activity. If you are faced with a genuine threat, you can almost always act to deal with it, relieve it, or avoid it. But worry or anxiety about some potential risk or threat over which you have no control serves no purpose and is a waste of time. Many people find their energy is completely sapped by continual worry.

Most things we worry about never happen. Even if they did materialize, they are unlikely to cause a catastrophe. Most events we worry about are losses that might cause us to change our way of living and to experience stress. We've already learned that there is no such thing as absolute security and that a healthy, optimistic man or woman can adjust and adapt to almost any foreseeable change.

Many changes actually turn out for the better. People faced with loss or change often discover that as one door closes, another door opens. If a dreaded event does occur, it frequently can open a door to something new and better. Whatever is going to happen, worrying about it won't make the slightest difference.

Every worry concerns a fear about the future. Very few of us are actually in danger or are being threatened at this moment, right now. All our fears concern some future event: tomorrow, next week, next month, next year. Few of us can find anything to worry about concerning the present moment.

So why not live in the now and enjoy the moment? Right now is the future we worried about yesterday, last week, or last year. And right now everything's fine. There's nothing to worry about. Worry occurs only when we start future-ing.

It is irresponsible not to make prudent preparations for the future. And we *should* be concerned (not worried) about potential threats that the future seems likely to hold. But when we have acted to make whatever reasonable preparations are within our power, it is counterproductive to our health and well-being to keep on future-ing.

Many worries arise out of the need to make a choice about which we have insufficient information. The obvious solution is to act and obtain the needed data. If you cannot find out all you need to know and must still make the choice, then use your intuition and choose the course that seems to harmonize most closely with loving, nurturing, and helping all of the people involved in the situation, including yourself. Through acting and making a loving choice, you end the reason for worrying. Through acting you also end any feeling of helplessness. Type C personalities are often so fearful of making a choice that they simply freeze and become immobilized whenever they must make an important decision.

For various reasons, in modern society it is not always possible to act to end a worry. Instead, we can often eliminate worry by doing something that will cause our mind-computer to overlay the negative worry-provoking thought with a worry-free positive thought. Here are some mind-action techniques that people have used to banish worry and anxiety.

Naturally, if you're worried about the health or possible death of a loved one, their worth should not be downplayed. But you can often take the worry out of other fears of loss by putting in proper perspective the importance of the object you fear losing.

Joe and Dorothy Brown were worried about losing their cabin cruiser because of difficulties in meeting the payments. Joe fretted about the possible loss. But Dorothy looked back and realized that ever since they bought the boat they'd been worried about its being damaged or stolen and about difficulties in getting spare parts.

"What value does it really have?" Dorothy asked. "It's been nothing but a burden."

Joe agreed. As soon as they had mentally downgraded the value of the boat, they stopped worrying. What they had previously feared losing was suddenly of no more value.

Rose Simpson found herself unable to sleep because of her worries. Just before bedtime she would make a list of all her fears and describe the worst that could happen in each case. Then she drew several thick lines across the page and fell soundly asleep.

A married couple tried the same technique. They made a list of every disaster that could possibly befall them. Their list included air and car crashes; leprosy; becoming deaf, dumb, and blind; losing all their limbs; cancer; heart disease; the loss of their jobs, home, car, and money; and enormous bills for taxes and medical care.

Their idea was to allot five minutes each day to worrying about their fears. However, they found it all so preposterous that they burst out laughing. They fairly rocked with laughter. They looked at each other and they laughed till their ribs ached. Whenever they bring out the list, they roll helplessly on the floor in paroxysms of mirth. They still haven't got around to worrying about the list.

Another twist on this method is to make a list of everything you were worried about a month ago. Then describe what happened to each fear. Chances are they've all melted away.

Yet another way to stop worrying is to do something more pleasant than worrying. Consider going to a party, making love, playing tennis, reading a novel, or any number of enjoyable pursuits. Another good way to take your mind completely off your own worries is to help someone who is in a worse position than you are.

Still another powerful mind-action technique is to imagine that the feared event has already occurred. Visualize what is frightening you. Picture yourself confronting it. For example, tell yourself that your stocks have plummeted and all your money has evaporated. What would you do? A quick evaluation might show that if you give up your vacation and sell some gold coins you could replace the loss. Or picture yourself in the feared situation. Hold it for a minute. Then open your eyes and realize you are perfectly safe after all. Repeat this exercise several times at regular intervals and the fear will gradually subside.

If you fear the dark, visualize yourself camping out alone in a forest at night. Picture yourself experiencing dark places without being afraid. Quite soon you are likely to feel an inner urge to test out your newfound freedom from fear by actually camping out alone in the woods at night.

Don't bury any fear. Keep it out in the open. Share it with others. You may meet someone who has experienced the thing you fear and who can assure you that it is not nearly as bad as you believe.

Write down your fears on paper and analyze the real risks. Estimate the conservative odds on a feared event's actually occurring. Most fears are so irrational and improbable that the actual odds they will ever occur are typically around one in a hundred or more. Write down how you would act to solve it if the fear ever did materialize.

You can detach yourself from fear of money loss by getting rid of any possessions or anything else that has actually become a burden, that is enslaving you, and that is hindering your liberation from stress and unhappiness. Beyond needing a place to live, a car, furniture, and money to provide for necessities, it becomes compulsive to keep on earning more and more money to buy more and more things.

Demonstrate to yourself how happy you could be with less money by making a list of activities you enjoy that are free. Condition yourself to loss by deliberately giving $10 (or $100, or more) to a deserving cause. Instead of judging your success by your net worth, try totaling up the amount of good you are accomplishing and how much happiness it is actually bringing you. Rate your self-worth by the number of successful relationships you enjoy.

In all these examples what has basically happened, of course, is that a primitive expectation has been transformed into a rather-belief.

Rather-belief: "I do not expect to always have my possessions. I would rather have those things that help enrich my life, that help me grow, or that I can share with others. But if for some reason I can no longer have them, I shall not be upset or unhappy. A loss isn't a loss if I never really expected to own or keep it in the first place. As to other fears, although I would rather that life ran completely smoothly, I do not expect it to be free of setbacks and obstacles. However, since I can now confidently deal with stress, I welcome setbacks as experiences that will help me grow. I will harmonize with and flow along with any changes to which I must adjust and I will enjoy the stimulation of the changes themselves."

Anger, hate, resentment, and frustration.   Americans as a group are angrier than ever. Inflation, the energy shortage, and soaring prices for homes, food, travel, and other everyday items have made people feel cheated. Many of us feel that life will never again be like it was before 1973. Younger people feel frustrated and angry because they cannot enjoy the same low-cost homes and energy that their parents had.

Anger, hate, and frustration can often be quickly rendered harmless in this way: Place your awareness on the site of the emotion. Anger for many people often seems to be located in the solar plexus, the pit of the stomach. Recognize and acknowledge that you are feeling angry. This will keep the anger surfaced. Then ask, "Why am I angry?" As the answer comes to you, the anger will subside.

Resentment is the most damaging of the anger-spectrum emotions. Resentment is long-term maintenance of anger. Like anger itself, it arises when a person fails to conform to your primitive expectations. You then feel wronged and you try to get even. To continue to bear resentment to the point where you feel you can never forgive another person is almost guaranteed to produce a serious physical illness.

Resentment, hate, grudges, and ill will exist to some extent in almost every Type A and C personality. These negative emotions are often deeply repressed and overlaid with an outward mask of friendliness and non-chalance. But deep within the body, the fight-or-flight mechanisms work their insidious damage, and cancer is all too often the result.

Rather-belief: "I would rather forgive than commit slow, involuntary suicide. Thus I forgive, now and forever, everyone who I believe may have caused me harm. This means everyone! I also forgive myself for bearing resentment and for any mistakes I may have made in the past."

You can intensify your forgiveness by visualizing the person you formerly resented receiving an abundance of love and good health. Picture him or her looking good and being successful. Also consider writing the person a letter expressing goodwill and friendship.

To forgive someone may be a painful act, but forgiveness is the only antidote to resentment.

Other forms of anger, hate, and frustration can be readily turned off by identifying the primitive belief that is responsible and by transforming it into a rather-belief. "Although I would rather have gasoline at thirty cents a gallon like my parents did, and a home I can afford, I will not become upset because these things are so expensive nowadays. Instead I will place greater value on other things like bicycling, a healthful way to get around that is much more acceptable now than in my parents' day. Meanwhile I will keep visualizing a reasonably priced home on my inner movie screen. Working subliminally, my mind-computer will find a way for me to get it."

The Dynamics of Positive Emotions

The most vital step you can take toward improving your health and recovering from disease is to replace your negative emotions with positive feelings of joy, love, gratitude, and humor. These powerful healing emotions turn on the body's calm state. Your nerves relax, your blood pressure drops, your hands and feet become warmer, and you experience a wonderful feeling of peace and well-being.

All that is necessary to put them to work is to reprogram your belief system with the new-beliefs in chapter 5 and to understand the dynamics of positive emotions. That done, positive emotions just naturally become a permanent part of your life.

Love. In 1979 the Field Research Corporation conducted a survey on behalf of the Office of Prevention of the California Department of Mental Health. After interviewing one thousand adults they found that those who were more loving and caring toward other people and who had a higher acceptance of others were twice as healthy, both physically and mentally, as people who were not caring, loving, and accepting.

Among all factors that contribute to health and long life, love is the most enriching. It is the core of life for most Type B personalities. And it takes precedence over every other health-building factor in reversing disease. Billy Graham considers love the most powerful force in existence. To love and be loved, he says, is the greatest experience in life.

To love therapeutically means to love everyone without reservation. The type of love that heals does not recognize love based on primitive expectations. Conditional love—for example, "I'll love you if you'll go bowling with me two nights a week"—is based on an expectation that, if not fulfilled, will arouse a negative feeling.

Love that heals translates into caring for a person and being concerned for that person. It means listening carefully to everything he or she says and feels. It means being open, honest, and truthful and sharing your deepest feelings with the other person. It means accepting other people the way they are without trying to influence, change, criticize, compare, evaluate, or manipulate them. Regardless of what people do or say, you accept that they are free to do or be what they like. And you never judge whether they are right or wrong.

Real love, the type that makes you well, allows no discrimination between loving one person and another. You love everyone without reservation. Even if a person is scornful or hostile, you greet that person calmly and with love. People are usually hostile because they lack love; so meeting a hostile person is an opportunity for you to give love to someone who so obviously needs it. Yet primitive beliefs program us to withhold love from such people because we expect them to be friendly and loving toward us.

Love cancels out and completely nullifies most stress. Stress causes us to alienate ourselves from one another, to compete on a me-versus-them basis, to think in terms of humanity against nature, and to view other people as threats. Love, in contrast, unifies people. Loving people realize that everyone is on the same path toward inner growth and that we are all really one. Love and oneness are the same. Instead of competing, loving people share. They regard things as "ours" rather than "mine or theirs."

That loving people are healthier and have lower blood pressure than self-centered people was demonstrated by Dr. Larry Scherwitz, assistant professor of community medicine at Baylor College in Texas. His tests proved that the more a person used the words "I, me, my, and mine" rather than "we, us, and ours," the greater the risk of high blood pressure. Another study by the Social Security Administration showed that virtually every American who reached the age of one hundred in active good health had a warm, loving, and generous personality. A detailed breakdown of their composite personality traits reads like a review of the new-beliefs in the previous chapter.

To enjoy optimum health we should inject love into every phase of our lives and actions. We should strive to become increasingly loving. Love should become the central theme of our lives. If we love everyone without reservation and accept them the way they are—without conditions or expectations—it is quite difficult for another person to upset us. The term *enemy* exists only as a primitive belief. As we reprogram our mind-computer with new-beliefs, we will find it easy to inject love into everything we say and do.

Just to be sure you do not slip up and forget, use the self-remembering technique to remind yourself to forgive readily; to be compassionate and sympathetic; to give and help freely; and to have reverence and concern for every living thing. Do this and stress will become nonexistent. People and events will cease to appear hostile or threatening, and your whole environment will become beautiful and friendly.

You can use this same philosophy to make yourself lovable. When you talk with someone, maintain eye contact. Encourage the other person to confide in you. Let other people feel safe in trusting you with their feelings. Encourage others to be open and honest, even to revealing their weaknesses to you. Maintain the strictest confidence about what you learn. To be loved, of course, you must make yourself available to another person. So set aside ample time for sharing interests, feelings, and conversation with a person who is prepared to give you love. Listen carefully to what the other person says. Don't interrupt or look around. Stay there and don't try to rush off. Sit close to the other person and touch or hug if you can. Remember that healing love is universal love. That means it is free of all expectations, conditions, and desires.

How does this differ from being in love with a member of the opposite sex? Technically, being in love with a member of the opposite sex is known as pair-bonding. It also is powerfully therapeutic. Numerous studies have shown that being in love, or being happily married, can improve health, reverse disease, and extend life.

A study of 10,000 Israeli men conducted by Dr. J. H. Medalie a few years ago in collaboration with the National Heart, Lung, and Blood Institute showed that men who had loving spouses or lovers had an appreciably lower rate of angina attacks and that men with unloving wives suffered a higher rate of heart attacks. The study, conducted over a five-year period, showed that men with loving wives had a lower angina rate even when they had very high blood pressure or cholesterol levels, or were overweight. Still another study demonstrated that women with loving husbands experienced less anxiety and less stress.

Falling in love has triggered the reversal of almost every kind of disease. Suddenly, the person in love is possessed of boundless energy, enthusiasm, and high spirits. Time flies. And becoming sick is extremely rare.

Records show that married people live longer and are healthier than singles. Generally, only people who have been married live to reach one hundred in fit and active condition. Why then do so many marriages and love affairs end in disaster? So many marriages and love affairs break up or end in divorce because the lovers, or at least one, fails to love without reservation. He or she falls in love with an expectation of what the spouse should say, feel, do, and be. Usually a person expects the spouse to share and reciprocate love so that they become as one. When the spouse fails to conform to this expectation, the person feels rejected.

To be successful, pair-bonding love should also be absolutely free of reservations. Each lover should accept the other totally and should not try to change, criticize, evaluate, or manipulate the spouse. Whatever the spouse says, feels, believes, or does is perfectly OK, within mutually acceptable limits. Each lover agrees to be completely open, honest, and truthful, to have no secrets, and to share all feelings. Each lover is concerned and caring about the other, listens carefully to what the spouse says, and takes time to share in the spouse's interests and problems.

When a relationship is free of all primitive beliefs and expectations, universal love and pair-bonding love are equally therapeutic.

Gratitude. In the memory banks of many sick people is a persistent belief that they should feel dissatisfied and sorry for themselves. These negative emotions trigger a low-level fight-or-flight response that can smolder indefinitely. This destructive attitude can be permanently reversed in a matter of minutes by substituting gratitude in place of self-pity.

You can readily experience gratitude by making a list of things for which you should really feel grateful. This can include commonplace things you take for granted like an easy chair and a fireplace, a stereo or TV, a family, a good book, a place to live, everything you have going for you. It should include being alive and having good health, loving friends, good food, warmth, clothes, a pleasant view, and so forth. Mentally experience each item as you read your list. You'll find it hard to go on feeling sorry for yourself or to be dissatisfied. As you progress, tell yourself you are also grateful for everything—good or bad—that happened to you today. Without a few setbacks you'll never grow; you need occasional obstacles as learning experiences. Remind yourself that everything you have is a gift and you'll never feel sorry for yourself again.

Humor, laughter, fun. Everybody knows that laughter is the best medicine. Numerous studies have proved that laughing and having fun relax tension and help recovery from disease. In 1964 Norman Cousins, editor of the *Saturday Review,* made a complete recovery from what was medically diagnosed as a terminal illness by watching slapstick comedy films and laughing his way back to health.

Laughing and having fun are tremendously beneficial emotions. Only you can choose to begin seeing the humor in everything and transforming yourself into a fun person. You can certainly begin by having a good laugh at yourself and by watching films and TV shows that really make you laugh. After that, seek out fun and enjoyment. Life is primarily a fun game. So learn to dance, skate, sing, act, bowl, or play an instrument.

Stand in front of a mirror, make a face, and wiggle your ears. Have a hearty laugh at yourself. If you ever feel frustrated get rid of the frustration. Then have a good laugh because you're no longer frustrated. Think of all the primitive beliefs you've programmed out and have another laugh because they can no longer upset you.

7. How to Build a Strong and Unconquerable Will to Live

YOUR GOALS and aspirations reveal more about your health than a whole set of diagnostic tests. During their studies of patients with terminal cancer, Carl and Stephanie Simonton found that people with strong and clearly defined life goals recovered better from all diseases, including cancer. They found that in planning to meet a goal, a patient was subconsciously reaffirming that he or she expected to live long enough to fulfill it. The mere act of deciding to reach a goal affirms that a person is in control of his or her life and is playing an active role in making things happen.

A Social Security study of American centenarians revealed that virtually every one always had a goal to work toward. Throughout their lives, as they attained each new goal, they invariably had another goal to strive for. The study showed that healthy, long-lived people almost never run out of goals.

Our goals represent all our hopes and aspirations. They are our reason for being alive. Each goal is a life wish and the sum total of our goals is our will to live.

Most people die because they lose their will to live. Studies show that elderly people frequently live until they reach a certain landmark event, typically the date of their granddaughter's graduation or their son's wedding or a birth in the family. When they realize their goal, they just give up and die. A person who runs out of goals runs out of will to live.

Having one or more goals establishes a meaning and purpose for living. Goals give direction to our lives. Our goals also determine our self-image, which is the picture we have in our minds of our inner self. Your inner self can best be described by answering the two questions Who am I? and Where am I going? Obviously, the answers are closely intertwined with your goals. But what really counts in promoting good health is your self-esteem or self-worth, meaning how you yourself feel about your self-image.

Only when we genuinely like and love ourselves—meaning our self-image—can our whole person begin to experience high-level wellness. Not until we love ourselves can we successfully give and receive love. An important prerequisite to genuinely loving another person or being loved by someone else is that we must first learn to accept and love ourselves.

Goals and a positive self-esteem are probably the strongest motivations to recovering from disease and returning to optimum health. A strongly positive self-esteem can provide a powerful new direction toward better health and recovery from disease. High self-esteem can only be based on a strongly positive self-image. People with high self-esteem appreciate their minds and bodies. They do not abuse the human organism with junk food, junk thoughts, or toxic stimulants or drugs; they exercise to keep their bodies lean and slim. They believe in themselves and they take it for granted that they are OK and beautiful. Almost all Type B people think highly of their self-image. By contrast, Type C's often have a poor self-image and low self-esteem with almost no goals.

Your self-image is composed of beliefs, thoughts, and mental pictures about who you are and where you're going. As we believe, think, and imagine, so we become. A person whose inner self is based on positive new-beliefs invariably has a positive self-image. A person whose inner self is based on outdated beliefs and expectations frequently has a negative self-image.

Because our inner self is often buried deep in the subconscious, most people are not really aware of who they are or where they're going. Without these answers, we cannot plan worthwhile goals or determine the true direction of our lives. So one of the most important health-building steps we can take is to find out exactly who we are and where we're going.

Strong, clear goals give meaning, purpose, and direction to life. Hopes and aspirations provide the reason and desire to go on living. The stronger and more noble, satisfying, and worthwhile are our goals, the stronger is our will to live. We must never run out of worthwhile goals. It's important to have a variety of goals to keep striving toward, not only for the immediate future but also for the more distant future.

INNER HEALING TECHNIQUE #7
Getting to Know Your Inner Self

Finding out who we really are and understanding ourselves have been goals of philosophers through the centuries. Who is the self that our mind chatters to? Who is the awareness we can place anywhere in our body? Who we are is actually the lifetime collection of experiences, conditions, and beliefs that combine to form our personality.

We can obtain an approximate profile of our personality by answering a series of questions designed to bring out hidden responses from deep within the subconscious. By answering the following questions, which are standard among new-age psychologies, you should be able to put together a fairly complete profile of your inner self. Use a separate sheet of paper for each question and don't be in a hurry. It may take several days for some of the answers to emerge. A few brief, possible answers to each question are given in parentheses.

1. Make a list of things, people, and activities that are really important to you. For example, walk through your home and ask yourself what it reveals about your real values and priorities. If your home caught fire, which ten items would you rescue first?
(My wife and son. Our securities and bankbooks. My cameras. The dog.)

2. Regardless of your age, answer: "What do I want to be when I grow up?"
(An organic farmer. A chiropractor. A novelist.)

3. Make a list of things you enjoy doing most.
(Family backpacking trips. Painting in oils. Shopping at garage sales.)

4. Make a list of everything you would do if you had only one day to live; seven days to live; three months to live.
(One day: make love, meditate, have a gourmet dinner.)

5. List the ten most important things you are in life.
(Husband, father, big brother to Bob, an architect.)

6. Imagine you are a film star being awarded an Oscar. What role would you have played and in what movie?
(Lawrence in *Lawrence of Arabia.*)

7. Make a list of things you least enjoy doing.
(Cleaning house. My work as an accountant. Commuting.)

8. List the things you like most about yourself.
(My body: lean, sinewy, athletic. My ability to relate to young people.)

9. List the things you like least about yourself.
(I am insensitive to feelings that others seem to experience readily. I overeat. I smoke.)

10. Which animal do you feel you most closely resemble?
(Seagull, eagle, dog, cat, bull, squirrel, hog, horse.)

11. If you had to wear a sign around your neck, what would it say?
(Love me! Notice me, I need your approval!)

12. What were the five happiest occasions in your life?
(Going on our honeymoon. Counseling young people in prison.)

13. Write out your obituary as you would like your life to be described in the local newspaper. Base it on what you would like to have achieved, not necessarily on your actual achievements.

(Brian Watson switched careers in mid-life to become a minister in the inner city. Through his unstinting efforts, he gave new hope and inspiration to hundreds of young people, directing them away from drugs and crime and toward developing meaningful vocations. His personal life was built on love, altruism, and service to humanity. After retiring ten years ago, he continued to work actively to help save America's wildlife from extinction and to spread love, warmth, and friendship among elderly shut-ins.)

14. Briefly describe what you learned from three people who influenced your life before age 20.

(George C., scoutmaster, taught me honesty and truth and how to survive in the wilderness; helped me realize I could become anything I wanted to become.)

15. Picture yourself at a reception held in your honor by ten close relatives and friends. Each gets up in turn and tells what he or she likes about you. Note what each person says.

(You're hard to know but you finish what you start. You can organize and get things done.)

16. Do you prefer to be alone or with others? What kind of person do you prefer as a companion?

(I enjoy walking alone in the mountains. As a companion, I prefer a physically active member of the opposite sex who enjoys outdoor recreations and sharing experiences.)

17. What were your three most enjoyable vacations and why?
(Studying yoga in India—it changed my whole life.)

18. How would your life change if you suddenly acquired a large sum of tax-free money, enough to retire on, for example?

(I would donate a tenth to charity. I would continue to work, stay in the same house, and keep the same car.)

19. What were the three most embarrassing moments in your life?
(When I was caught cheating during final exams. When I was caught shoplifting.)

20. If you were to become sick, what benefits would it bring you?

(I would avoid having to go on working at a stressful and monotonous job. I could avoid having to make love with my spouse, an insensitive lover. I would receive love, care, and sympathy from my family, which I don't get right now.)

21. Could any of the benefits which you listed in #20 be achieved without your becoming sick?

(I could change jobs. I could get a divorce. I could make myself more lovable.)

Putting your answers together should reveal a fairly complete picture of what your real values and priorities are. You may learn that you are spending an excessive amount of time and effort playing a game, maintaining a role, or trying to prove you are right and someone else is wrong.

If your answers indicate you would quit your present job if you could, your job is probably a source of stress. You may also learn what you would rather be doing instead. If acquiring a large sum of money would cause few, if any, changes in your lifestyle, your present life is probably stress-free and satisfactory. Again, listing the benefits you could obtain through becoming sick is another way of defining what you really want out of life. All too many people actually become sick as the only way to get what they really want. When it is pointed out how they could get these same things without becoming sick, they often recover with surprising speed.

When a friend of mine, a British travel writer, answered the twenty-one questions, they revealed a long-forgotten goal that was still running much of his life. Fifty years ago, when he was nine, he met a young girl of the same age who was vacationing in England with her parents. The girl's home was a tea plantation in Ceylon. It all sounded very exciting and exotic to my friend. He felt intensely envious of the girl who, although only nine, had already traveled through much of Europe and Asia. At that point, he decided to devote his life to traveling to every country in the world so that never again would he be made to feel inferior by someone who had been to more places and had had more exciting and exotic experiences than he had.

Fifty years later, he was still running his life by the same goal. He had been divorced three times because his extensive travels took him away from home so much. Answering the twenty-one questions revealed to him that he had finally outgrown the need to be always making others feel envious by his constant travels.

"It wasn't until now that I discovered my life is still being run by a belief and by a goal that dates back half a century," he said. "I've grown and matured to where I'm out of step with what I'm doing. Travel is no longer fulfilling or challenging."

The writer explained that he had also been taking medication for high blood pressure for the past five years. "Answering the questions brought out the conflict that exists between what I'm doing and what I'd like to do," he said. "I'm sure this emotional conflict is causing my hypertension."

A month later, he obtained a transfer to an editorial job in London, which involved no further traveling. He was able to exercise daily and to eat a low-fat diet. Gradually, his blood pressure returned to normal and he was able to stop taking his medication.

What did your personality profile reveal? Can you identify any changes you made by accepting some or all of the new-beliefs in chapter 5?

Turning Death Wishes into Life Wishes

By defining your goals, you can do more to strengthen your will to live than any drug or health technique can. But not all goals are equally effective. For maximum holistic benefit, we should have goals that call for physical activity, for mental activity, for cultivating positive emotions, and, if possible, for spiritual growth.

The more noble, challenging, and satisfying the goal, the greater its overall benefit to your health. A goal with a high-quality purpose that makes maximum use of your talents and abilities has a far more beneficial effect on your health than a goal to go fishing every day. However, we also need fun and relaxation. For maximum satisfaction, we should have a variety of goals that include career goals, recreational goals, fun goals, growth goals, goals to strengthen family ties, goals to develop love and romance, and goals to widen our social contacts.

It is important to know exactly what each goal is. Avoid vague ideas such as "I'd like to be a writer." What sort of writer? A travel writer? A health writer? Don't just say "I'd like to lose weight and become slim." Be more specific: "I'd like to lose twenty pounds over the next ten weeks through a combination of low-fat diet and long daily walks."

Most new-age psychologists believe we should have at least nine goals: three near-term goals; three mid-term goals; and three long-term goals. As we fulfill each goal, we should have another goal ready to replace it.

Based on these guidelines, how would you plan three goals to be attained within the next ninety days; three more to be fulfilled within six months; and three others to be attained within a year? Here is a sample list made by a forty-year-old married man after reading a draft of this book.

Three-Month Goals

1. Attain emotional calm and serenity. Live in the calm state all of the time.
2. Accept all the new-beliefs. Create a self-image I can really accept and love.
3. Improve my marriage relationship. Spend a second honeymoon in Florida this March.

Six-Month Goals

1. Seek at least ten new, satisfying relationships, including getting to know my relatives and in-laws better. Invite my wife's brother and his family for a vacation at our home in July.

2. Beginning now and progressing over the next six months, start a gradual exercise program designed to eventually have me jogging a full hour five times a week. On the other two days, do yoga asanas.

3. Learn all about nutrition and other health factors so that I can stay healthy and live as long as possible. Become a vegetarian.

Twelve-Month Goals

1. Quit my job as an accountant, sell our home, buy a place in the country with land, and become a self-sufficient organic farmer.

2. Rent out the house each winter to skiers and spend the winter in a rented apartment in Mexico.

3. Take courses in disco and square dancing. Go dancing twice a week. On other nights, invite people over. Enjoy life, sing, dance, play, hug, relax, and have fun.

Choose goals that are attainable. Avoid goals that would depend on another person's cooperation (other than your spouse or family, and, in that case, work out the goals with them). For example, don't build a goal that depends on someone's loaning you money or on a relative's dying and leaving you an inheritance. On the other hand, don't let uncertainties like the state of the economy, the weather, or not having a car deter you. Use technique #1. Psych yourself up into the win-power state. Decide exactly what you want and where, when, and how you're going to get it. Then *go for it!*

As you learn more about your inner self, you'll also probably discover that you are already on the way toward some of your goals. But you had to find out who you were and where you were going to realize your real purpose in life. Often, you can upgrade already existing goals by injecting them with new-beliefs and other ennobling qualities.

The higher the quality of your goals, the stronger will be your will to live, your ability to recover from disease, and your desire to achieve robust health and long life.

Again, any goal is better than no goal. So if you would still prefer a goal like going fishing every day, then by all means do so. If the thought of spending every day fishing or playing golf or whatever gives you a good feeling and provides something to anticipate with eagerness, then it has definite therapeutic value. You may eventually become tired of fishing every day. But by then, you can have another goal worked out. Any goal to which you can eagerly look forward strengthens your will to live by the amount of your enthusiasm.

A beneficial goal doesn't have to involve a major life change or risk taking. Something as simple as taking a thirty-minute walk five times a week is a valid goal. So are making a dress, learning to swim, buying a boat, taking a trip, or taking a course in public speaking. A goal that takes you into a new, unfamiliar area or activity provides a spark of adventure that can add zest to living. Striving toward a new goal such as learning to dance or traveling abroad can also widen your social contacts.

Of course, you must also start taking active steps to fulfill each goal. Make a list of action-steps you will take within the next month toward attaining each of your goals. You needn't be working toward all nine goals at once. But you should have some constructive ideas about how to achieve the first two or three. Use the list of action-steps as a guide to how you will spend some of your time during the next three months.

Nothing breeds success like success. So consider breaking up large goals into smaller increments. Instead of losing twenty pounds in ten weeks, consider losing two pounds every seven days. A small bite-sized success every seven days is a powerful incentive to keep on losing weight.

INNER HEALING TECHNIQUE #8
Creating a Positive Self-Image

Add together your goals and your picture of your inner self and you already have a fairly complete profile of your self-image. Your self-image is your picture of who you are and where you're going. It is also your mental blueprint of what you will be in several months or a year or more. It is your master plan of what you are in the process of becoming. As you believe, think, and imagine you are, so you will become.

Stop and take a look at your self-image. To do so, take six sheets of paper and place one of these headings on each: physical; mental; emotional; spiritual; goals; beliefs. Under each heading, list all the qualities that you found out about yourself when you answered the twenty-one questions. Add any others that you know of. List your goals. List all the pros on the left half of each sheet, the cons on the right.

For example, under *physical* you might list the following. Pros: clear skin; full head of hair; good eyesight, hearing, smell, taste; free of arthritis and other physical ailments; able to walk three miles before becoming fatigued. Cons: smoke ten cigarettes a day; lack lung power and endurance; flabby, mediocre energy reserves; eat too much fat and sugar.

How do you appraise your self-image? Do you like yourself? Dislike yourself? Feel ugly? Feel OK? Feel beautiful?

Most often, you will discover that you like your self-image in some areas and not in others. You may like your emotional self but dislike your physical self. How well do you like the overall picture? Can you love your self-image?

If you have already reprogrammed yourself with new-beliefs and positive emotions, and if you are now unaffected by stressful life events, you will most probably have a very strong self-image with high self-esteem. If you are still programmed by outdated beliefs, still attached to security, ego-power, and possessions, and dependent on them and on external events for happiness and satisfaction, you will probably have a negative self-image and low self-esteem.

If you cannot like and love your self-image, you have things in your life that need programming out. These are negative factors that you cannot accept. They are creating an emotional conflict within your subconscious. If they haven't done so already, in all probability they will eventually make you sick.

To love yourself totally, you must get rid of all negative goals, beliefs, expectations, habits, and physical factors that you dislike about yourself; and you must replace them with positive goals, beliefs, habits, and physical factors that you can accept, like, and love. The good thing about your self-image is that if you are not happy with it, you can easily create a new blueprint for yourself that you do like and love.

So take six more sheets of paper, write out the same six headings, one to a sheet, then list all the positive factors you would like to incorporate into your new self-image. Your physical list might now read: lean, slim, flexible, youthful, athletic build; sinewy, well-defined muscle tone; nonsmoker, abstainer from all stimulants; unlimited energy and stamina; able to run six miles, swim two miles, do physical work all day and still dance in the evening; sharply dressed; teeth in good repair; diet consists entirely of natural high-fiber foods with minimum of fat, sugar, and salt; superhealthy; never feel sick or have a pain, even for a brief period.

Now put together all of your positive factors: physical, mental, emotional, spiritual, goals, and beliefs. Your list will probably include all the new-beliefs in chapter 5 and all the positive emotions from chapter 6. The result will be a totally new you that you can accept as OK and beautiful and that you can like and love totally.

If it isn't, then keep working on your new self-profile until it does have all the features you want. Create a powerfully positive self-identity that you can accept and love without reservation.

Use your existing strong points and positive personality factors as building blocks. Congratulate yourself for already having these good points and begin loving yourself for them right away. (A person who cannot list any positive factors has a very low self-esteem, often to the point where his or her health is in danger.) Then forgive yourself for your weaknesses and love yourself because you can forgive. If you have accepted some of the new-beliefs and positive emotions from preceding chapters, you should already have an impressive list of good points.

Don't be afraid of boasting in your list. No one else need see it. Build the framework of your new self-image around your existing strengths, potentials, and talents. Then translate any existing weaknesses or imperfections into new, strongly positive factors.

Remember that your self-image is what *you* think, believe, and imagine about yourself. It is not what others think of you. Nor is it your occupation or the roles and games you play. It is not the way you compare yourself or your accomplishments with those of others. It is not your past mistakes.

Your new self-image should entirely eliminate any roles you are acting out. Instead of seeing yourself as an architect, businessperson, jogger, or socialite, see yourself as you naturally are.

Some people find it simpler to model themselves on a guru or other highly evolved person. They are able to identify with, accept, and imitate the physical build, beliefs, emotions, and behavior of their model person. Almost all of us know someone we admire who is highly motivated and who enjoys life without being affluent. Consider reading a biography of someone you'd like to emulate.

Some yoga masters have already prepared self-image blueprints for their followers. The following holistic outline, in which Swami Satchidananda states the goals of integral yoga, is a model of conciseness. "A body of perfect health and strength, mind with all clarity and calmness, intellect as sharp as a razor, will as pliable as steel, heart full of love and compassion, life full of dedication, and Realization of the True Self."

As you list the positive factors that will make up your new self-image, visualize yourself about to be reborn. Regardless of what you are now or of past mistakes, life begins anew each day.

This very evening, read your list and visualize yourself being reborn tomorrow as a nonsmoker, a slim, healthy person, and a calm, poised, happy, loving person. Use win-power (technique #1) and mindshift (see chapter 5) to get you started on this inner work. You'll also find it helpful to write out afresh each day the list of positive factors that you wish to incorporate into your new self-image.

The more you can accept, like, and love your new self-image, the higher will be your self-esteem and self-worth. The higher your self-esteem, the closer you become to a disease-resistant Type B personality.

Continue to maintain a high appreciation of your new self-image. Think highly of your body, yourself, and all your abilities. Love yourself as a whole person. Believe in your self-image. The more you do, the sooner you will actually become your self-image.

What happens then? When you and your self-image are identical, you will love yourself as well as you love your self-image. Most healthy people love themselves already, of course, because their real self and their self-image are virtually identical.

However, many Type A and C personalities are unable to love themselves because of their poor habits of thinking, living, and eating, such as smoking, being overweight, ill-tempered, angry, hostile, aggressive, rude, or unloving. Since it is easier to correct these imperfections in the imagination than in reality, you can start accepting and loving your new self-image long before you can accept and love yourself the way you are.

Let's say you are thirty pounds overweight and you hate yourself for it. Almost immediately, you can change your self-image and picture yourself as thirty pounds lighter, which means you can begin loving your self-image right away. For therapeutic purposes, loving your self-image is as beneficial as loving yourself.

Once you do become your self-image, you need only keep reprogramming your goals so that you always have some nine goals to strive for. If you like and love your new self, that's just fine. Accept the new you and be content. You need only change your self-image if you find anything you dislike in the person you currently are.

INNER HEALING TECHNIQUE #9
Mapping Your Health Goals

For those who may not be adept at making mental pictures of their self-image and goals, Unity church recommends making a "treasure map." What you do is paste onto a large sheet of cardboard a variety of pictures—photographs or illustrations from magazines—that depict you having already fulfilled your goals.

Let's say you have osteoarthritis in the knee. You'd cut out color pictures of people who resembled you running along a beach, bending their knees in flexible yoga postures, climbing mountains, pedaling bicycles, swimming, or using their knees in ways free of stiffness or pain.

Since you'd probably also want to lose weight, you'd paste a recent photo of yourself in a before-and-after context next to a picture of somebody who resembled you but was lean and slim. Even better, cut out your own face and paste it onto the body you desire.

A picture of a greasy steak and egg dish would be crossed out with a *no, no* sign. Dotted around would be pictures of tempting fresh fruits and vegetables. Then across the top, in large cut-out letters, would be spelled, "I am completely free of arthritis. My weight is 155."

Making a map forces you to spend time and effort clarifying your goals and thinking about how to achieve them. You'd keep the map in your bed-room where, night and morning, it would reinforce your self-image. The Unity church advises its members to use vivid pictures and large type and to paste the cut-outs onto a large, stiff sheet. For additional reinforcement, church members are advised to write out their goals each morning while repeating the words out loud (or saying them silently if others are present). You might also record your goal phrases on a cassette tape and play the tape each morning.

Over the years, Unity headquarters in Missouri has received thousands of reports from people who have recovered their health or achieved other life goals through "treasure mapping."

Although it is often said that your mind-computer will operate sublimi-nally to find a way to achieve whatever goal you map or visualize, you can significantly speed up the process if you already know exactly how your goal should be achieved.

Symbolizing Your Self-Image

Guided imagery, described in chapter 11, is the most widely used inner healing technique. One stage of this process consists of visualizing strong reasons for becoming well. The reasons are expressed by our goals. In other words, we should visualize our self-image. It goes without saying that the stronger and more positive our self-image, the more effective is the healing power of guided imagery.

Since the subconscious mind communicates in images and feelings rather than in words, the best way to visualize our self-image is through a symbol. The symbol should harmonize with nature. It should depict love, calm, wellness, energy, and other new-belief qualities. Typical symbols are a seagull, an eagle, a dog, a cat, and a horse. Or you might choose to see yourself as a bicyclist, cross-country skier, walker, jogger, swimmer, or hang-glider pilot. You may prefer to be a stream or river or a canoe, rowboat, or sailboat. A friend of mine likes to think of himself as a brook flowing on through life to eventually become one with all great waters.

I see myself as a calm, loving bicyclist riding up and down adventurous mountain roads toward a final Shangri-la. Almost any symbol will do pro-vided it is nontechnical and travels silently in a calm, free-flowing way using only its own energy. It should symbolize movement: you want to flow, fly, sail, drift, walk, pedal, swim, or ski your way toward higher and better things.

Although a symbol for your own self-image may not occur immediately, one will invariably appear. Visualize your symbol often so that your subcon-scious recognizes it as your self-image.

8. *Progressive Relaxation: Escaping the Tension Trap*

WHEN ANYTHING UPSET Mary Turner, she would be depressed for several days. She felt tense and upset and would often not speak to her husband for twenty-four hours. By her mid-thirties, Mary had an ulcer and her stools would be black for several days following each upset. Tranquilizers helped, but they left Mary listless and enervated. Eventually, her doctor referred her to a local pain clinic.

There a therapist taught Mary how to transform her positive tension into negative tension in exactly eight seconds. Mary also learned how to relax both her mind and body so that only a few minutes after becoming upset, her hypothalamus would turn on the calm state.

At first, Mary's ego resisted her using the technique; she felt that she ought to feel angry and upset. But her tension continued unabated and she promised her therapist she would use the technique the next time she became upset. Her next upset wasn't long in coming. She was in a department store when a salesman made a chauvinistic remark and Mary exploded. A minute later, she realized she was headed for four more days of misery. Right away, she pinched her left wrist and called out "Stop! Stop!"

Then Mary stood stock-still and did absolutely nothing. She began to take the first of twelve slow, deep breaths that her therapist had told her would calm her. As she did so, she slid aside the thought that the salesman had offended her. In its place she visualized herself walking along a tropical beach. As she completed the twelfth deep breath, she clenched her fists and tensed every muscle in her body as hard as she could. Her face was screwed up tight, her toes were curled, even her tongue was pressed hard against the roof of her mouth. Slowly, she counted from one to eight. Then she let go.

The technique Mary used is an emergency form of self-induced relaxation known as deep muscle relaxation, the relaxation response, or, as I call it, progressive relaxation. It worked so well that within a few months Mary's ulcer had vanished and she has had no recurrence of the black stools.

Turning Positive Tension into Negative Tension

Progressive relaxation is a technique for achieving disciplined body relaxation. It employs physical and mental relaxation techniques simultaneously to guide your mind and body into the calm state. It is the basis of all biofeedback and is one of the most powerful and effective inner healing tools. Progressive relaxation is widely used in pain clinics to relieve tension and provide rapid relief from high blood pressure, lower back pains, and migraine and tension headaches.

Proof of its effectiveness was reported in the October 1977 *American Journal of Public Health* in an article describing a study by Dr. Herbert M. Benson of Harvard Medical School. Benson divided 126 employees of the Converse Rubber Company into three groups. The first group was taught to use progressive relaxation twice a day for fifteen minutes. The second group was asked to sit quietly twice a day for fifteen minutes. The third, or control group, was given no instructions at all. During the twelve-week observation period, blood pressure dropped in all three groups but the drop was significantly larger in group one. Benson also reported an impressive decrease in the incidence of all sickness in group one.

Thirty-five years ago, progressive relaxation would have been dismissed as a branch of voodoo. It was employed only in yoga, hypnosis, and a few obscure autogenic training systems. But with new, sensitive electronic instruments, modern technology finally proved that progressive relaxation not only works but is often more successful than drugs or psychiatry. Progressive relaxation demonstrates immediately that we all do have some control over our bodies and that we need not be helpless victims of disease. You discover you can relax your entire body at will, eliminate all tension, and guide your whole person into the calm state. In the calm state, your mind does not experience worry, anxiety, or fear.

Progressive relaxation employs three steps, each of which helps you gain control over an involuntary body function. As the basic law of biofeedback reminds us, "Not only does every change in thought cause a corresponding change in body function, but also every change in body function is accompanied by a corresponding change in our feelings and thoughts."

The steps are: physical relaxation; deep breathing; and mental relaxation.

When a potentially stressful life event is interpreted as threatening or unfriendly by our outdated beliefs, the hypothalamus turns on the fight-or-flight response and our muscles are charged with energy and tensed for action. Unless we act physically to burn up this energy, the tension remains. Tension builds up in our voluntary muscles, those striated muscles attached to the skeleton that we use to move at will. Each muscle is capable of rapid movement and is controlled by a nerve. In many people, particularly Type A's, the voluntary muscles are kept in a half-tensed state during much of the day. This semipermanent state of contraction saps energy and causes constant fatigue.

Through progressive relaxation we can learn to disassociate our voluntary muscles from the controlling nerves and relax them. Deep breathing helps us relax the autonomic nervous system, which in turn relaxes the plain or unstriped involuntary muscles. These muscles surround all our body ducts, including the blood vessels, sphincters, and alimentary canal. They relax and contract slowly and are controlled by the autonomic nervous system. As both our autonomic nervous system and involuntary muscles relax, the blood vessels dilate, the circulation improves, the pumping load on the heart is reduced, and the blood pressure drops.

Whenever our mind-computer identifies input as stressful, our brain wave enters the beta state, identified by a fast and excited frequency of 13 to 30 cycles per second. This state of conscious thinking is turned on whenever we feel even slightly tense or emotionally upset.

Through progressive relaxation we can dispel negative thoughts and feelings, release tension, and voluntarily place brain activity into the relaxed alpha state. Our mind-computer then slows brain-wave activity to 8 to 13 cycles per second. This is an altered state of consciousness that we seldom experience.

In the alpha state, the mind is free of all mind-chatter and other interference from its rational operation. When we are in the alpha state, our conscious mind is subdued and in direct communication with the subconscious. During this relaxed state, the subconscious is able to accept vivid and powerful images of the state of health (or any other goal) that we wish to give it.

Through progressive relaxation, we can induce the calm alpha state at will. Compared to positive tension, which triggers multiple states of distress, the alpha state creates negative tension, a delicious feeling of detachment from the worries and pressures of living. As you become increasingly relaxed, the mind disassociates from the body and you become entirely unaware that you have a body at all.

You are experiencing the calm state, the state in which, ideally, we should function all of the time. In this state, the parasympathetic branch of the autonomic nervous system is running the body and maintaining routine metabolism. As blood lactate levels drop and tension disappears, negative thoughts and feelings are unable to exist in the mind. The pulse rate drops, respiration slows, and oxygen consumption falls. The white blood cell count increases and the immune system becomes steadily stronger and more aggressive. Our pain threshold rises and we become increasingly able to tolerate pain. We feel comfortable, at ease, and in a state approaching high-level wellness.

In this easeful state, we are unlikely to ever become sick. Being in the calm state helps the autonomic nervous system stabilize and rebalance all involuntary body functions (commonly known as body chemistry).

Some of us may have come close to experiencing the calm state after having exercised vigorously and then lain on the grass or beach as we focused our entire awareness on listening to relaxing music; or during meditation; or after a sexual climax; or, perhaps, through lying in a "tank," completely deprived of sensory stimulation.

But for many people, the alpha state is a new experience, far beyond the kinds of relaxation we think we experience. Although many of us consider TV relaxing, actually it is often quite stressful. Except for humorous programs or soothing music, TV shows and commercials seldom create relaxation. Since we tend to identify with people in sports, drama, commercials, news, and programs depicting violence, most programs create stress. TV also robs us of the opportunity to think, act, and do things for ourselves and it atrophies our power of imagery. As it turns adults and children into passive spectators, it intensifies our feelings of helplessness. If you've been wondering how to find time for inner healing techniques, here is the solution: stop watching all TV programs except those that make you laugh or that are genuinely educational.

The mind states induced by alcohol and drugs are not satisfactory substitutes for the calm state induced by completely natural means. Alcohol and drugs produce a temporary insensibility that destroys the powers of imagery and concentration, rendering the mind completely incapable of using guided imagery or other inner healing techniques.

(A word of caution: if you have serious heart disease, hypertension, osteoporosis, or any other condition that might be affected by tensing your muscles, check with your doctor before starting any of the following progressive relaxation exercises. But be aware that unless your doctor is prevention-oriented, you are likely to be given biased advice.)

Progressive relaxation should be practiced only in a quiet place where you will not be disturbed. The exercises are divided into three steps, but you will do them one right after another. At first these three steps might take a total of fifteen minutes, but eventually you will be able to achieve a deep level of relaxation in just several minutes. (After you are experienced and comfortable with techniques #10-13, you can move on to the shorter versions of physical relaxation in techniques #14-19.)

INNER HEALING TECHNIQUE #10
Progressive Relaxation
Step One: Physical Relaxation

Physical relaxation is achieved by tensing each muscle in the body, one by one, as hard as possible for approximately eight seconds, then releasing. This burns the stored-up energy that is keeping each muscle tense and contracted.

While you are tensing and releasing each muscle, place your awareness on that muscle and visualize a warm, comfortable color like orange or pink. Visualize each limb and muscle area bathed and suffused with this color as you tense and release it. If you prefer, you can visualize each muscle bathed in brilliant sunshine.

Even the briefest negative image in the mind will produce a minute contraction of muscles around the eyes, face, forehead, and jaw. So be sure to thoroughly relax these areas. Breathe normally as you tense and relax each body part.

Lie flat on your back on the floor or bed, a pillow supporting your head, your arms and legs uncrossed and stretched to their full length. Keep your hands about eight inches from your body, your legs a few inches apart. Keep arms and legs straight.

Begin by raising your left hand six inches off the floor. Clench the fist tightly. Keep the arm straight. Then tense the muscles all the way from the shoulder down the bicep and forearm to your fist. Tense them all simultaneously as hard as you can and hold to a slow count of eight. Then release and drop your arm loosely back to the floor. Let your hand remain open.

Repeat with the right arm.

Raise the left foot six inches off the floor. Tense the entire limb from buttocks to toes. Hold to a slow count of eight. Then release and drop loosely to the floor. While tensing, you can curl the toes to make sure you tense your foot.

Repeat with the right leg.

Next, tense both buttocks together. Hold for eight seconds and release.

Then tense the abdomen muscles and release.

Tense the back muscles and release.

Tense the chest muscles and release.

Push the back of your head against the pillow and arch your neck and back off the floor or bed. Hold for eight seconds and release. Roll your head loosely from side to side a few times and relax.

Tense your whole face and scalp by screwing up your face and eyes tightly. Hold for eight seconds and release.

Go over the face again and separately tense and relax the scalp, forehead, eyes, cheeks, tongue, and especially the jaw. Keep visualizing the warm color, or brilliant sunshine, suffusing each of these areas as you place your awareness on them and tense and release them.

Then let yourself sag and go limp all over.

INNER HEALING TECHNIQUE #11
Progressive Relaxation
Step Two: Deep Breathing

Deep breathing relaxes the autonomic nervous system and slows the brain wave to the alpha frequency. You should still be lying on your back on the bed or floor after having completed step one. Don't pause after completing step one but just flow straight into step two.

Begin by breathing slowly and deeply, in and out, at the rate of six breaths per minute. Now that your chest and abdomen are relaxed, you can completely fill the lower and upper areas of your lungs. Gradually slow the rate of breathing to only four breaths per minute. As you breathe, visualize the same warm color or bright sunshine as in step one. See it suffusing your lungs and spreading rapidly through the rest of your body. Visualize the color or sunshine flowing in as you inhale, and flowing out as you exhale.

Complete twelve deep breaths. At this point, you should be well into the alpha brain-wave state and ready to flow into step three.

INNER HEALING TECHNIQUE #12
Progressive Relaxation
Step Three: Mental Relaxation

This step uses both imagery and suggestion. Both work best when your attitude is relaxed. You are not giving yourself orders, so avoid any intense or compulsive feeling. Just place your awareness on the limb you wish to relax. Silently say the suggested phrases to yourself and create a mental picture of the limb deeply relaxed. Then just let it happen. Don't try to force or hurry anything. If a daydream intrudes, slide the unwanted thought aside and return to your imagery.

Part of the exercise consists of visualizing warmth spreading through your body. Along with the warm feeling, you can also picture the same warm color or the bright sunshine you visualized in step one.

Step three consists of mentally creating a feeling of warm comfort and pleasure that begins in the soles of your feet and spreads upward to your head and face. Then you deepen the relaxation by visualizing another warm wave of pleasure moving from your head back down to your feet. This leaves the whole body in a deep state of negative tension.

You should still be lying flat on your back in the same position in which you did steps one and two.

Place your awareness on the sole of your right foot.

Say to yourself: "My body is relaxed and my mind is quiet. I feel a small patch of warmth on the sole of my foot about the size of a quarter. Now the warmth is spreading out over the sole of my right foot. It is spreading all over my foot and up through my ankle. It is moving slowly up my calf. My calf feels pleasant and comfortable as the warm, heavy feeling spreads upward. My calf muscle is heavy and warm and completely relaxed. The warm feeling is spreading up through my knee into my thigh. A wave of warmth and pleasure is spreading up my thigh and into my buttock. My thigh and buttock feel heavy and warm and pleasant and comfortable. Now my thigh and buttock are completely relaxed."

Naturally, as you silently say the words you are visualizing this relaxed feeling of warmth, comfort, and pleasure moving slowly up your calf toward your knee and then to your buttock. You don't have to use these exact words.

Repeat the same process with the left leg and buttock. Then let the wave of warmth and pleasure flow up to relax the abdomen: "My abdomen feels heavy and warm. I feel comfort and pleasure and warmth in my abdomen. Now my abdomen is completely relaxed."

Let the warmth flow up through your body, relaxing the back and chest muscles. Then, starting from the shoulder, let it flow down the right arm to your fingertips. Repeat with your left arm. Let the heavy, warm feeling flow up your neck and up over the back of your head into the scalp. Relax your scalp deeply. Then let the heaviness and warmth creep down your forehead to your eyes. Spend some time deeply relaxing the eyes and the area between them. Let the wave of heaviness and warmth spread down your face to the mouth, tongue, and jaws. Deeply relax the jaw muscles.

Now, starting from the jaws, let your awareness slowly work back in reverse over the same body areas it has just covered. This time, you repeat only the words "Relax! Relax! Relax!" At the same time, visualize tension flowing out of each muscle like air escaping from a tire. Then visualize the muscle as limp and relaxed as a piece of old, frayed, worn-out rope, or as limp as a rag doll or a jellyfish.

Begin with the jaws and repeat with the tongue, face, eyes, forehead, scalp, and neck. Relax each arm beginning at the shoulder and ending at the fingertips. See tension flowing out of the fingertips. Picture the arm as limp and relaxed as a deflated inner tube.

Work down through the chest and back muscles to the abdomen. Relax the left leg, starting from the buttock and going down to the sole of the foot. Then repeat on the right leg.

Next, place the awareness in turn on the lungs, heart, liver, pancreas, digestive organs, and bladder as you say "Relax! Relax! Relax!" With a little practice, you can relax an entire limb or organ as you slowly say the words.

Finally tell yourself, "My entire body is totally relaxed. My whole body feels warm, heavy, comfortable, calm, and relaxed. My mind is quiet and serene. My whole person is in the calm state."

At this point, your body is in a deep state of negative tension and your mind is in a deep alpha state, not thinking of anything in particular. You are ideally prepared to flow naturally into one of three altered states of consciousness. All three can be used for inner healing. They are meditation (technique #21); self-hypnosis (technique #23); and guided imagery (technique #26).

INNER HEALING TECHNIQUE #13
Learning to Recognize Negative Tension

By learning to identify positive tension, you can tell immediately whenever tension exists in a muscle. Conversely, you can also recognize whenever a muscle is relaxed and in a state of negative tension. By practicing the following exercise, you will learn how to remain in a state of negative tension at all times.

Lie flat on your back and go through steps one, two, and three of progressive relaxation (techniques #10-12) so that you are deeply relaxed. Lift the wrist of your right hand so that the hand is raised off the bed or floor. Hold it there. Immediately you will experience positive tension in your right forearm. Place your awareness on the tension. Experience it completely. Ask yourself how it feels. What is it like? What color does it suggest? What shape is it? Does it suggest a smell or taste? Does it remind you of any event or condition from the past? Does it prompt a mental picture? Can you hear anything in your inner ear?

Place your awareness on your left forearm. Experience the negative tension. Does it suggest a smell, taste, feeling, memory, color or sound?

Switch your awareness back and forth from negative to positive tension. Learn to recognize the dull ache of positive tension. Compare it with the delightful feeling of negative tension.

Drop your right hand and relax it again. Next, clench your left fist tightly and raise it. Now your left forearm has positive tension, your right forearm negative tension. Compare both again and ask yourself if either one suggests a smell, taste, feeling, memory, color, or sound.

If either state creates a sensory experience, you can re-create that same state of tension by visualizing the sensory experience on your inner movie screen. Let's say that as you experience negative tension, you keep seeing a mental picture of yourself lying in the sun on a beach. You hear the soft, rhythmic murmur of gentle surf. You smell the salty tang of drying seaweed. Your fingers touch the warm grains of sand. Now project this same scene onto your inner movie screen. Make a clear and vivid picture of yourself lying in the sun on a beach. In your inner ear, you hear the murmur of light surf. Your nostrils are filled with the salty tang. Your fingers run through the warm grains of sand. As you create this scene, you will immediately experience a deep state of negative tension. The more vivid the picture and the more realistically you create the sounds, smell, and feeling, the deeper and more satisfying will be your state of relaxation.

When you move this overall scene and feeling to an area where you are experiencing tension, the tension should promptly vanish. What's happening, of course, is that at some previous time—perhaps as a child—you lay on a beach while deeply relaxed. As you re-create this scene, your mind-computer takes you right back into the same deep state of relaxation you originally experienced.

Alternatively, you may find that positive tension evokes an equally deep memory. You might see yourself working on a production line. You smell ugly fumes, taste acrid smoke, and hear endless crashing noises. Any time you experience a similar industrial scene—either real or imagined—in all probability your hypothalamus will trigger the fight-or-flight response and you will experience positive tension.

From these experiences, you can learn to induce negative tension at any time by creating a scene like the beach scene. And you can learn to avoid producing tension by taking care not to visualize or experience a scene like the production line scene. Should you have to work in a situation like a production line, you can relieve the tension by creating a calm scene like the beach scene in your imagination as often as possible.

Go over every pair of opposing muscles in your body, tensing one while relaxing the other. Muscle by muscle, experience positive and negative tension all over your body. Recognize and identify the various feelings. Go over your shoulders, neck, face, and jaw, searching for pockets of residual tension. As you discover them, relax them until you experience total negative tension.

Deep Relaxation in Less Than Two Minutes

Once you can identify positive and negative tension, you can spend less time on muscles that relax easily and more time on areas where tension tends to linger, typically the face and jaw.

After your first few attempts with each of the three steps to progressive relaxation, you should find yourself flowing smoothly from one step into the next without pause. After a few weeks, many people learn to attain total relaxation in one to two minutes. You can significantly speed up physical relaxation by using one of the following techniques. Each achieves the same deep level of physical relaxation, but in a shorter time than technique #10.

Continue to breathe normally while tensing and relaxing. Don't forget to keep visualizing the same warm color, or bright sunshine, that you visualized in step one of progressive relaxation. Try to visualize your whole body filled with this color or sunshine as you tense it. As you release the muscles, say "Let go!"

INNER HEALING TECHNIQUE #14
Physical Relaxation: Half-Body Tensing

You can do this exercise either standing up or lying down. First, tense all the muscles below your waist. Hold for eight seconds and release. Second, tense all the muscles above your waist. Hold for eight seconds and release. If standing, lie down on your back. Roll your head loosely from side to side a few times. Last, go over the scalp, face, eyes, and jaw to make sure you have released all tension in your head.

INNER HEALING TECHNIQUE #15
Physical Relaxation: Whole-Body Tensing

You can also do this exercise standing up or lying down. This time, you tense every muscle in the entire body at once. Hold for eight seconds and release. Then, lying on your back, roll your head loosely from side to side a few times. Last, go over the scalp, face, eyes, and jaw to make sure you have released all tension in your head.

INNER HEALING TECHNIQUE #16
Physical Relaxation: Full-Body Tensing
with Abdominal Contraction

Lie on your back on the floor or bed, head supported by a pillow. Next, sit upright. Hold your arms straight out in front. Keep your legs straight and together, and raise your feet twelve inches off the floor. This will force you to lean back a bit. Then tense every muscle in the body for eight seconds and release. Drop back flat on the floor or bed and relax. Roll your head loosely a few times from side to side. Last, go over the scalp, face, eyes, and jaw to make sure you have relaxed every muscle in your head.

For still deeper relaxation you can, if you wish, repeat any of the physical

110

relaxation techniques a second or even a third time. Or you might consider doing a combination of techniques #10, #13, #14, and #15 one time each.

The following are two speedier methods for combining steps two and three into a single technique. Pick the one that works best for you.

INNER HEALING TECHNIQUE #17
Combined Deep Breathing and Mental Relaxation

Take the same slow, deep breaths (six per minute) as in technique #11. But as you begin to inhale the first breath, place the awareness on the sole of your right foot. Visualize yourself "inhaling" through the skin of your right foot, ankle, and calf. Then picture your breath being "exhaled" through the same area. Next, visualize yourself inhaling and exhaling through the skin of your right thigh. Continue with the left foot, ankle, calf, and thigh.

Then, muscle by muscle, visualize yourself inhaling and exhaling through the buttocks, abdomen, back and chest muscles, each arm (separately), neck, scalp, and face. If you detect any positive tension remaining in the face or jaws, take an extra breath or two to release it.

Gradually, slow your breathing from six breaths per minute to four. As you inhale, visualize the warm color or sunshine flowing into each muscle. As you exhale, feel each body part become increasingly relaxed.

INNER HEALING TECHNIQUE #18
Combined Deep Breathing and Relaxation Counting

Take the same slow, deep breaths (six per minute) as in technique #11. As you inhale the first breath, visualize a large figure 10 on your inner movie screen. Silently say "ten." As you exhale, visualize the figure 10 flashing on and off like a neon sign. At the next breath, change to figure 9. Then breathe and count each number down to zero. Gradually reduce your breathing rate from six breaths per minute to four. By the time you reach zero, you should already be in a deep alpha state.

With practice, you can reduce the number of breaths required. A combination of techniques #14 and #17 provides a swift way to relax and achieve a calm state at any time. However, if you are emotionally upset to begin with, the following technique is more effective.

INNER HEALING TECHNIQUE #19
Rapid Relaxation Response

Whenever you feel overwhelmed by tension or unable to cope with stress, use this emergency technique to restore the calm state.

1. Pinch your wrist and call out "Stop! Stop!" (Do it silently if others are around.)

2. Do nothing. Slide aside the thought that is on your inner movie screen. In its place see an image of yourself detached from whatever is causing the stress. Or visualize a beautiful beach or garden scene. Regardless of what is causing the stress, forget it. It doesn't matter. Instead, take six slow, deep breaths. As you do, silently repeat to yourself: "It doesn't matter. It's not important. It's only harming my health. So I'm going to forget it entirely. Nothing is worth getting sick over. I am completely detached from the thing that upset me." Use your own words, of course.

3. Do technique #15. That is, as you stand erect and breathe normally, tense every muscle in the body as hard as you can for eight seconds, then release. Follow this with six short, deep breaths.

In as short a time as sixty seconds, these three simple action-steps can transform a state of deep positive tension and distress into a calm state of negative tension. To induce still deeper relaxation, continue with the following action-steps.

Repeat action-step 3 once more, including the six slow, deep breaths.

4. While sitting or standing, let your head drop loosely all the way forward. Then slowly roll it completely around in one direction, then in the other direction. Repeat six times.

5. Rotate your shoulders loosely ten times in one direction and ten times in the opposite direction.

6. Raise your shoulders up to your ears as high as you can. Hold tightly for five seconds, then drop. Repeat five times.

7. Screw your face up tightly, clench your jaw, and press your tongue against the roof of your mouth. Hold for eight seconds, then release.

8. Press the palm of your right hand against the right side of your face and try to twist your head to the right while you resist it with your arm. Put your full effort into this isometric exercise. Hold eight seconds and release. Repeat on the left side.

9. Place both hands, palms up, under your chin. Press your head and chin down as hard as you can while pushing up with your arms. Hold this isometric position for eight seconds, then relax.

10. Clasp both hands at the back of your head. Push your head backward as hard as you can while you resist the pressure with your arms. Hold this isometric position for eight seconds, then relax.

Once you reach the calm state, you can deepen your relaxation still further by practicing technique #20 in the next chapter.

9. Inner Healing for Headaches and Hypertension

CHRIS WICKHAM had suffered for years from recurring migraine headaches. Each attack brought an intense throbbing pain in his forehead and behind one eye, a pain so excruciating he was often driven to bed for twenty-four hours.

The headaches seemed to be triggered by emotional stress or by eating foods high in fat or salt. Over the years Chris had tried every remedy from aspirin to narcotics, but nothing was able to prevent the attacks.

Finally Chris's doctor sent him to a new pain clinic at the local hospital. At the clinic, Chris learned that migraine headaches can be triggered by a variety of physical, mental, or emotional stimuli that cause an arterial constriction, cutting off oxygen from the nerves on one side of the head. The pain occurs as the arteries dilate to increase the flow of oxygen-bearing blood. Chris learned that three inner healing techniques can provide dramatic relief for both migraine and tension headaches, regardless of the cause of the headaches. And because high blood pressure is also caused by vasoconstriction of the arteries, the same techniques are widely used in biofeedback training to reverse hypertension.

First, Chris was taught progressive relaxation. After only two weeks he was able to attain the calm state in just a few minutes. At this point, he was instructed to change over to muscle tensing. The therapist gave Chris the choice of any muscle-tensing technique, provided it was done standing up (techniques #10, #14, #15, and #16 in this book).

Chris then began to warm his hands and feet (technique #20). After practicing thirty minutes a day for two weeks, he could raise the temperature of his hands by eight degrees Fahrenheit.

A month after his first visit to the pain clinic, Chris was practicing only two techniques. He would begin by standing up and tensing his whole body for eight seconds, using technique #15. Then he would rest twenty seconds and repeat the tensing a second time. Immediately afterward he would lie down and perform technique #20. He did this combined exercise only once each day, before breakfast. Then at noon and again in the evening, he would tense and release all his muscles twice, using technique #15. Chris was pleased to discover that his daily exercises occupied only fifteen minutes before breakfast and another minute at midday and again in the evening. He felt this total of seventeen minutes was a small price to pay for freedom from headaches.

Beginning exactly thirty days after he first attended the pain clinic, Chris began to experience migraine attacks only half as often. Whenever he felt an attack coming on, he would immediately tense and release all his muscles by performing technique #15 twice. He found no difficulty in tensing his muscles, even when sitting at a desk. Then at the first chance Chris would warm his hands, using technique #20, which he could also do while sitting upright at his desk.

By using one or both techniques at the first hint of a headache, Chris found he could squelch almost all headaches before they could take effect. And if a headache did begin, the two techniques done together brought almost certain relief.

The inner healing therapies the pain clinic recommended were based on important research developed by biofeedback specialists.

First was a study done at Columbia Presbyterian Medical Center, which proved that tensing each muscle in the body for fifteen seconds and releasing it provided dramatic relief from 80 percent of all headaches, both migraine and tension.

Second, scientists at the Headache Research Treatment Project at the Menninger Foundation found that progressive relaxation followed by warming the hands completely relieved migraine headaches in 75 percent of all sufferers. Their studies revealed that migraine sufferers frequently have hand temperatures that are ten degrees below normal. They also found that when deep relaxation and hand warming are practiced at the first sign of a migraine attack, 80 percent of all attacks can be circumvented. Among their successful cases were patients with migraines too stubborn to be controlled by even the strongest narcotics.

Similar results were obtained by Broino Kiveloff, M.D., of the New York Infirmary, who pioneered the use of muscle tensing to relieve hypertension. Kiveloff had his patients tense every muscle in the body for six seconds, then release. His technique was comparable to technique #10, #14, #15, or #16 in this book.

Whichever technique you choose, you should repeat it twice, holding for eight seconds and releasing as we suggest. Or you can duplicate Kiveloff's times and perform the exercise three times, tensing each time for six seconds before releasing.

Even repeated three times with a twenty-second break in between each time, you can easily do the entire tensing routine in seventy seconds. The exercise should be repeated in the morning, at midday, and again in the evening.

It takes five to eight weeks of regular daily muscle-tensing practice before elevated blood pressure will begin to drop. After the blood pressure has returned to normal, the muscle-tensing routine must be continued indefinitely. Even if you don't have hypertension, the exercise provides good insurance against your ever having elevated blood pressure. Tests have shown that 90 percent of hypertensives have been helped by muscle tensing. Warming the hands and feet is also standard biofeedback therapy for hypertension. Thus, whether you have headaches or hypertension, muscle tensing combined with warming the hands and feet should provide positive results.

If your fingers and toes are often cold, it is probably a symptom of tension-caused stress. Stress triggers the autonomic nervous system to constrict arteries and the smaller arterioles all over the body, diminishing circulation to the extremities. You can usually identify this condition by learning to recognize positive tension.

If you have neither headaches nor hypertension, you can use technique #20 as a substitute for progressive relaxation. Once you have learned to warm your hands, you will probably no longer need to go through steps one, two, and three of the progressive relaxation routine. Eventually, many people discover they can skip progressive relaxation altogether and use hand warming instead.

How Hand Warming Works

This important inner healing therapy should be practiced regularly by anyone suffering from high blood pressure, atherosclerosis, heart disease, muscular tension, poor circulation, chronically cold hands and feet, and migraine or tension headaches. People with elevated blood pressure should begin to practice it as soon as possible, two or three times a day.

If you suffer from frequent headaches, practice muscle tensing followed by warming the hands and feet once a day as a preventive measure. Then twice a day at other times, practice muscle tensing alone. If you feel a headache coming on, practice both techniques immediately. In most cases, this action will abort the headache. Warming the hands and feet is also an effective antidote to muscular tension and is beneficial for all forms of cardiovascular disease.

When we learn to relax and visualize our hands and feet as warm, the blood vessels in our extremities dilate and more blood flows in, making our hands and feet warmer and heavier, just as we visualized. As nerves and muscles in one area learn to relax, the effect generalizes throughout the body. Blood is drawn away from scalp and brain areas as arteries in the arms and legs dilate, and the cause of most headaches is removed.

Because all body functions are related, as you learn to control a single body function, like warming your hands, the ability can be applied to other body functions. Gradually, the entire body learns to maintain a deeply relaxed state at all times.

You must become proficient at progressive relaxation before you can go on to warming the hands and feet. Once you can attain deep relaxation, it takes about thirty minutes a day to learn to raise the temperature of your hands by eight to ten degrees. But once you learn it, you can gradually skip progressive relaxation and achieve deep relaxation as part of the hand-warming technique.

INNER HEALING TECHNIQUE #20
Warming the Hands and Feet

To practice warming the hands and feet, you should lie down in a quiet place where you will not be disturbed. Progressive relaxation, described in chapter 8, is a prerequisite to warming the hands and feet. Once you are deeply relaxed in the calm state, you may then continue as follows.

Start by making a clear, vivid mental picture of yourself wearing trunks or a bikini and lying on a warm, sunny beach. There's a gentle breeze and only a few tiny tufts of white cloud fleck the blue sky. You feel the sun's golden rays warming you all over. You experience comfort and pleasure and your body feels heavy and relaxed.

Now have an imaginary person cover your hands and feet with white, sun-warmed sand. Place your awareness on your left hand. Feel your hand being warmed by heat from the sand. Visualize warmth radiating through your hand. Picture your hand as heavy and warm. As you do so, repeat these phrases: "My hand feels heavy and warm. I feel warmth flowing into my hand. I feel the warmth in my hand. I feel my hand becoming warmer. My hand feels quite warm. My hand is tingling with warmth."

Keep repeating the phrases. You don't have to use the exact words or memorize them. But say essentially the same thing. As you silently say each phrase, visualize a clear, vivid picture of each suggestion on your inner movie screen. Or just create the visualization out where your awareness is— in your left hand.

In a minute or two, your left hand should begin to tingle and feel warmer. When it does, repeat the same thing with the right hand.

Once both hands are tingling and feeling warm, you can deepen the feeling by changing your suggestions to include both hands: "My hands are heavy and warm. Warmth is flowing into my hands." And so on. Visualize both hands as tingling and warm.

Once your hands are warm, transfer your awareness to your left foot. Visualize a spot of warmth in the sole of your left foot. Picture it spreading out and over your foot right up to the ankle. Use the same suggestions, replacing the word *hand* with *foot.* When the left foot is warm and tingling, repeat with the right foot.

You will probably find that warming the feet takes longer and requires more practice. You may also find that one hand becomes warm appreciably faster than the other. If so, start with this hand. As soon as you feel tingling and warmth in this more suggestible hand, magnify the feeling. Then spread that same feeling to the other hand, and later to the feet.

You may find you can speed up the warming process by visualizing the red glow of a hot plate or hot coals inside your hands and feet. Or you might visualize your hands and feet plunged into hot water.

Be sure you are in a moderately warm room. Eventually, you may be able to warm your hands and feet when they are quite cold. But this takes practice. At first, the room temperature should not be below seventy degrees Fahrenheit. Never try to force or hurry anything. Just make the pictures and repeat the phrases.

Once you feel tingling in both hands and feet, you can rephrase your suggestions: "My hands and feet feel heavy and warm. I feel my hands and feet becoming warm," and so on.

As the blood vessels dilate in your hands and feet, more blood flows in, making your hands and feet heavier and warmer. During this process, you unconsciously sink into a deeper state of relaxation and suggestibility. Gradually, this condition generalizes and spreads through your entire body.

Once you can warm your hands and feet, you can speed up the generalization by warming your arms and legs. Begin by warming your forearms. When they feel tingling and warm, continue with the upper arms. Then warm your calves and later your thighs. Eventually you can warm your abdomen.

Assuming you practice hand warming for twenty minutes or so each day, if you're like most people you can probably warm your hands quite appreciably in seven to ten days.

You can monitor your progress by either taping a small room thermometer to the pad of your index finger so the bulb is in contact with your skin or, better, purchase a few liquid crystal strips from a local biofeedback practitioner, hospital, pain clinic, or medical supply outlet. Each strip has an adhesive backing that you stick along the inside of your middle finger. Once in contact with your skin, the strip glows with a color and number that you translate into a temperature reading with the aid of a chart. As you warm your hand, the glow indicates your exact temperature increase. Technically, the strips are known as psychological trend indicators or discrete readout thermometers. Though they gradually lose their sensitivity with use, I have used a single strip repeatedly. They recently cost only a few dollars apiece. One manufacturer is Medical Device Corp., 1555 Bellefontaine Street Drive, Indianapolis, IN 46202. This firm has sold small quantities to individuals by mail, but write for their literature before sending an order.

10. Taming the Mind

O NCE YOU HAVE ATTAINED deep relaxation, as
described in chapter 8, it takes only a brief period to
relax the mind and enter a meditative or self-hypnotic state.

INNER HEALING TECHNIQUE #21
Meditation

Meditation is a means of attaining the calm state by stopping all thought.
During meditation, your inner movie screen is blank. One does not meditate *on* something, as we hear people say they will meditate on a flower or
on a candle flame. What they mean is that they will hold an image of a
flower or candle flame on their inner movie screen to the exclusion of all
other thoughts. This is properly called concentration or contemplation. In
true meditation, the flow of restless thoughts is halted altogether. One has
no thoughts or images at all. The mind is totally blank.

When thoughts are stopped, so are feelings. As this altered state of consciousness occurs, the hypothalamus turns on the calm state and the body
enters a state of gradually deepening relaxation. This phenomenon was discovered several thousand years ago during the development of yoga.

Regardless of other appellations like Transcendental Meditation, the dis-
cipline of meditation is simply raja yoga. Raja is one of half a dozen different approaches through which a yoga student may attain unity with the
Absolute. Meditation is also used in Zen and other religious practices.

Although physiologically it is just another way to achieve the calm state,
meditation is associated with a mystical quality that gives it special value for
inner healing.

During the late 1960s and early 1970s, when Maharishi Mahesh Yogi
popularized meditation in the West, a number of studies demonstrated that

meditation did indeed induce the calm state. Dr. Herbert Benson of Harvard Medical School and Archie K. Wallace of UCLA both found that during meditation the body's entire metabolism decreases. Oxygen consumption is reduced by 10 to 20 percent, the mind shifts into the alpha brain-wave state, the pulse rate slows, and lactic acid production drops with a corresponding decrease in feelings of fear or anxiety.

In one study of thirty-six hypertensives, Benson found that after several weeks of daily meditation practice, the subjects' average diastolic blood pressure dropped from 93.5 to 88.9 and their systolic readings from 146 to 137.

A more recent study by Ronald Jevning at the University of California Irvine Medical Center found that during meditation blood flow to the brain increased by 35 percent. This may help explain why meditators report being able to think more clearly and why older meditators seldom seem to suffer from senility or mental degeneration.

But in all cases, benefits continue only as long as meditation is practiced regularly. When hypertensives stop meditating, their blood pressure returns to earlier levels.

For most people, progressive relaxation (techniques #10-12) is a more certain way of attaining the calm state. Having attained the calm state through steps one, two, and three, you can easily enter the meditative state by sitting upright and silently repeating a word like *om*.

Otherwise, you can enter a state of meditation in the following way.

Go to a room or place that is quiet and free of disturbance. Sit cross-legged on the floor, in the yoga lotus position if you can. Otherwise, simply cross your legs. Sit on a cushion if it is more comfortable. Alternatively, just sit in a chair with your arms and legs uncrossed. In any case, keep your back straight. Take six slow, deep breaths.

Then begin to silently repeat a word. You can repeat a mantra like *om* or *prem* or a longer one like *om mane padme hum*. Or you can simply repeat the word *one*. Phrase the word at a relaxed pace. Focus your awareness on repeating the word. If a thought slides onto your inner movie screen, slide it aside and bring your awareness back to repeating the word.

Alternatively, you can "watch" your breath. Breathe through your nose and place your awareness on your nostrils. "Watch" your breath as you slowly inhale and exhale. Keep your awareness entirely on your breathing. If a thought intrudes, slide it out of your consciousness. You may also repeat a mantra while breathing. The phrase *Hong saw* is often used. Slowly and silently say "hong" as you inhale and "saw" as you exhale.

In a few minutes you should feel the body relax, and if you stop repeating the word the mind will remain still. By continuously repeating a meaningless word, or by watching the breath, you distract your mind from thinking. Your mind-computer soon learns that thoughts just can't get through. So it momentarily stops trying.

All mind-chatter and disturbing thoughts have disappeared and you experience a deep feeling of inner peace. A typical meditation session lasts fifteen minutes from start to finish and should be practiced twice daily if possible. The more often you meditate, the sooner you enter the calm state. People who meditate regularly report a noticeable decrease in fear and anxiety and a heightened ability to think optimistic and positive thoughts.

From my own personal experience, as well as from discussions with teachers of raja yoga, I have concluded that meditation appears to be the best technique for permanently taming restless, racing thoughts and mind-chatter. Through meditation, people find themselves experiencing an altered state of consciousness that leads to a feeling of unity with a higher power. This mind state is often coupled with a revelation of new understanding and enlightenment. From a holistic viewpoint, such insight is obviously beneficial to health and well-being. Several people have told me that meditation helped them create a more receptive attitude toward accepting the new-beliefs.

The mystical quality associated with meditation enhances its suitability for use in an inner healing technique that involves contacting your intuitive guide (technique #22). While science may scorn the idea of subjective communication with the subconscious, pioneer researchers like Robert Assagiolli have developed techniques through which we can "ask" our subconscious for a diagnosis and also for healing advice concerning any ailment from which we are suffering.

Let's say, for example, that you have essential hypertension, a common form of high blood pressure for which medical science has no explanation. Nowadays, a growing number of new-age psychologists believe that we can ask our subconscious directly why we have high blood pressure. They also believe the subconscious can tell us what to do to reverse the condition.

The subconscious communicates with our conscious mind through intuition, feelings, images, or dreams. Thus we cannot directly ask, "Why is my blood pressure elevated?" Nor can the subconscious reply, "Stop smoking and exercise." It can reply only in the form of a symbol, image, feeling, intuition, or dream. To facilitate this communication, new-age psychologists have rejuvenated an ancient yoga technique called the intuitive guide.

INNER HEALING TECHNIQUE #22
Using Your Intuitive Guide

The intuitive guide is a ready-made symbol, an imaginary person or animal, to whom we can phrase questions for relaying to the subconscious mind. After an incubation period that may be as short as a few hours, the subconscious will reply in the form of intuition (a subtle inner voice), a strong feeling, an image, or a dream. Or the intuitive guide may even tell us the answer while we are in the alpha state or while dreaming.

To contact your own intuitive guide, first enter a moderately deep state of meditation. Next, imagine you are looking at a plain wall. Facing you in the center of the wall is a door. Now the door opens smoothly. Behind it you will see your intuitive guide.

As Jung discovered, your personal intuitive guide often turns out to be a figure from traditional folk mythology such as the Wise Old Man or the Great Mother. Or your guide may appear as a deceased person, as someone you once knew, or as a highly evolved person or religious figure. Your guide may also turn out to be a friendly animal such as a dog or rabbit.

Another way to contact your intuitive guide is to visualize a distant cloud coming toward you. As the cloud approaches, it takes the form of your intuitive guide. The presence of your intuitive guide should evoke a feeling of friendliness, comfort, and warmth. Ask your intuitive guide to tell you its name.

New-age psychologists believe that the guide represents our inner self or real self. Hence the guide symbolizes who we really are, how we are living, and where we are going.

Using silent, inner talk, you can ask your guide questions about your health and disease. You can ask for a diagnosis and for advice on how to reverse an ailment. You can also ask questions about your goals, self-image, thoughts, habits, and about changing your beliefs.

Using language that the subconscious understands (images, feelings), your guide will relay your questions to your psyche in the depths of your mind. It will also relay the answer. Sometimes the answer comes as an inner voice, as a mental picture, or in the form of a dream; sometimes the guide may appear and give you the answer directly.

Such communication occurs only when your brain wave is in the alpha state; or in the state of light sleep to deep reverie, the theta state; or during the even slower delta state, while you are sleeping.

At these times, the guide is likely to pass on healing wisdom or to reveal powerful messages from the subconscious that identify the source of a pain or a deep-seated emotion.

Perhaps half of all answers appear during dreams. Based on research in recent years, an entirely new theory of dream significance has emerged. Most psychologists now agree that dreaming takes place in the brain's right hemisphere, the nonverbal, emotional, artistic, and creative half of our mind-computer. Lacking in logical time sequence, the right hemisphere emphasizes visual and spacial strengths. Its activity is filled with images. The right hemisphere is unable to express its awareness in words. Hence all communications must be in the form of images, dreams, intuition, or a symbol such as the intuitive guide.

While dreaming, the right hemisphere is experiencing our inner self. And our inner self is trying to help us cope with problems concerning who we are, how we are living, and where we are going.

If we can learn to interpret the symbols, the answers to many of our health problems are in our dreams. One difficulty is that each person has his or her own individual dream symbols. We must look in our dreams for symbols that are frequently repeated. See how the symbol keeps recurring and in what context. Dream symbols are often extremely straightforward and simple. If you see yourself in a hot tub or sauna, your dream is probably saying nothing more than that you are a warm person. If you dream about being in ice or snow, the dream may be saying you are cold and unresponsive.

Prior to reading a draft of this book and accepting the new-beliefs, a friend of mine regularly dreamed about being back in the navy in World War II. He knew he could not escape being in this dangerous situation until the war was over. I interpreted this to mean that he was still trapped in a fear situation. Since reprogramming his belief system, he has not experienced a return of this dream.

Hundreds of writers, composers, and inventors make regular use of the right hemisphere's intuitive problem-solving ability. They feed facts and questions to which they seek answers into their mind-computer as they are dropping off to sleep. During a dream, or as they awaken, they often experience the answer they seek. Or it may come the following night or the next day.

By consolidating the input material, matching its files, and retrieving an answer, the right hemisphere provides us with the services of a free computer that anyone can learn to use.

You can make use of this same computer action to program the right hemisphere to change a recurring nightmare into a pleasant dream. While you are in the alpha state, recall the scene in the dream where the nightmare occurs. Place it on your inner movie screen. Now you can do one of two things.

1. Visualize many more people in the scene. Transform it into a Brueghel painting, filled with busy, but friendly people. If you can recall other scenes from the same dream, fill them with a large number of people. They should be repeated in your next dream. For some reason, the more people in a dream, the more pleasant it is.

2. Work out a pleasant solution to your nightmare. Visualize this happening in place of the recurring nightmare scenes. Repeat the visualization several times with strong, clear images.

If you have a dream that you cannot understand, re-create it during a guided imagery session. Your intuitive guide or your inner self may be able to help you find out what the dream is trying to tell you.

INNER HEALING TECHNIQUE #23
Self-Hypnosis

Self-hypnosis is a heightened state of awareness that deepens our ability to concentrate and increases our susceptibility to suggestion. You can very easily achieve the self-hypnotic state.

First, turn on the calm state by performing steps one, two, and three of the progressive relaxation routine. At this point, your body will be deeply relaxed and your mind in the slow alpha brain-wave state.

Then visualize yourself standing at the top of a long flight of stairs. The stairs lead down into a garden that surrounds the deep, transparent waters of a spring. Start walking down the stairs, at the rate of about one per second, counting as you go, one step per count. There are thirty steps to the bottom.

The lowest step brings you next to the deep, translucent spring. The clear water is at least a hundred feet deep. Now toss a shiny new dime into the spring. Keep your awareness about three feet from the dime as it flashes, darts, twists and turns on its way to the bottom. Down, down it goes, deeper and deeper into the still, silent depths. All is calm and quiet at the bottom of the spring. The dime rests on the sandy bottom and your mind is in a deep state of peace and serenity.

At this point, you should be in a state of light-to-moderate self-hypnosis. To find out if you are, place your awareness on your right hand. Then repeat these suggestions: "My right hand feels warm. In just a minute my hand will begin to tingle with warmth. I feel my hand tingling. The tingling is like pins and needles."

Keep repeating these suggestions while you make clear, vivid images of what you are suggesting on your inner movie screen. Keep repeating the suggestions and the pictures. In a very short time you should feel your right hand begin to tingle.

Once the tingling appears, magnify it. Feel it becoming like pins and needles. Tell yourself: "The tingling is becoming as intense as pins and needles. The tingling is stronger. I feel pins and needles all over my right hand."

In just a short time the tingling should intensify. This is an indication that you are in a state of light hypnosis. Now tell yourself: "I am going deeper and deeper into relaxation. I am becoming more and more suggestible. My mind will say yes to everything I suggest."

Place your awareness on your left hand. Visualize a cord around your left wrist leading up to a large helium-filled balloon. The balloon is exerting a powerful lift to your wrist.

Repeat these phrases as you visualize them: "The balloon is pulling my wrist strongly upward. My wrist is floating off the floor. My hand is as light as a Ping-Pong ball. My hand feels weightless. The balloon is raising my wrist off the floor. My wrist is rising off the floor. The cord is cutting into my wrist as it strains to lift my wrist off the floor."

Keep repeating these phrases as you make clear, vivid pictures of the large balloon overhead powerfully lifting your wrist up and off the floor.

Don't try to force anything. Stay completely relaxed and keep repeating the suggestions and making the mental pictures. Avoid any hint of intenseness or compulsiveness.

Gradually, in tiny jerks, your wrist will slowly levitate off the floor. Bit by bit, it will rise up to an angle of ninety degrees with your elbow.

At this point, tell yourself: "The cord is cut. My wrist is free." Visualize the cord being cut. Your wrist will drop back to the floor. If this hand-levitation test works, it is proof that you are in a moderately deep state of self-hypnosis and that your subconscious mind is carrying out all suggestions you give it.

Another way to check on the depth to which you have hypnotized yourself is to visualize a yardstick. On the yardstick is a sliding pointer. The pointer is free to slide up and down the yardstick and point at any reading from 1" to 36".

Now tell yourself: "The pointer will show my depth of hypnosis." On your inner movie screen, you will see the pointer float up and down the yardstick a few times then come to rest at a level that approximately corresponds with the depth of your hypnosis. Under 12" indicates a light state of hypnosis. Over 24" is a deep state. For most self-hypnosis activities, a light-to-moderate level is sufficient.

Many people find it helpful to "see" or "hear" the hypnotic suggestions coming from an authoritative person, an imaginary hypnotist. A Wise Old Man or a Great Mother figure is most commonly used. If you have used technique #22 to meet your intuitive guide, assuming the guide is an authoritative person you could visualize your guide giving you the suggestions. Or you might even visualize a stage hypnotist in tie and tails, with fierce mustache and gleaming eyes.

To use an authority figure, simply imagine the person looking down at you and making the suggestions. Instead of saying *"My* hand is tingling," the person would say *"Your* hand is tingling." You give your entire attention to the authority figure and you mentally say yes to everything he or she says.

How can self-hypnosis improve your health? In almost the same way as guided imagery, which is discussed extensively in the next three chapters. The dividing line between self-hypnosis and guided imagery is a thin one indeed. Both states are attained in the same way and both use imagery and suggestion to program the subconscious to carry out an intention.

Until a decade or two ago, self-hypnosis was more widely used. Since then, therapists have discovered that people accept guided imagery more readily. Many people still associate hypnosis with having power over another person or with forcing someone to do something against his or her will.

The fact is that nine out of ten people can learn to hypnotize themselves in just a few practice sessions. Self-hypnosis gives you power only to direct your own wishes into your own subconscious mind. In self-hypnosis, you have no contact with another person. Hence, no one can force you to do anything you would not normally do. Nor can you force yourself to do anything against your will.

Through self-hypnosis you can carry out almost all the imagery and suggestion programs described for use with guided imagery. Self-hypnosis differs from guided imagery only in that the tests described above to check your state of suggestibility are not used in guided imagery. In self-hypnosis, you can also employ an imaginary authority figure to give you the suggestions. Another difference is that in self-hypnosis suggestions often seem to be timed for the immediate future ("In just a minute my hand will tingle"), whereas in guided imagery suggestions are always phrased as though they had already occurred ("My hands are tingling"). Hypnotists feel that providing a short time lead gives the mind and body time to carry out the suggestion.

Self-hypnosis makes more versatile use of the mind-computer. By using suggestions and imagery, you can regress back to early childhood or infancy, where you can vividly relive a past happening. You will see, feel, hear, smell, and touch the scene as it originally was. You experience the original pain or fright. Through self-hypnosis, you can also retrieve long-forgotten memories. You can distort time. One hour can pass like one minute normally does. Or you can place one or more of your limbs, or your entire body, in a cataleptic (stiff) state. You can also learn to raise your pain threshold and induce some degree of anesthesia. These things might also be done through guided imagery, but they seldom are.

A definite advantage of self-hypnosis is the use of an authority figure to give suggestions that involve the breaking of an undesirable habit.

Let's say you wish to break a habit of overeating. You go into a light-to-moderate hypnotic state and on your inner movie screen you see your authority figure, say a Wise Old Man. You visualize in three-dimensional color everything the old man says. Here are some typical suggestions he could use: "You are going deeper and deeper into hypnosis. Listen carefully to everything I say. You will mentally say yes to everything I suggest. ... From now on, every time you eat a meal, by the time you are two-thirds finished, you will feel satisfied and full. You will feel no need to eat more. You will feel warm and full and satisfied. You will want to throw away the remaining one third of your plateful. You will have eaten all you need. You will enjoy feeling slightly hungry. You will enjoy the feeling of not being stuffed. You will enjoy the light, relaxed feeling of eating small meals. You will find it necessary to eat only when you are hungry. You will enjoy avoiding the task of digesting heavy meals. You will sleep better and feel better at all times."

These suggestions should be repeated at least four times while you continue to visualize each suggestion. Then your authority figure should wind up the session: "As I count backward from five to one, you will return to your normal state of consciousness. You will feel rested and relaxed and completely free of any ailment. You will enjoy hypnotizing yourself again. Next time, you will go into hypnosis faster and you will enter a deeper state. Five, four, three, two, one."

Memory recall and age regression are obviously useful in tracing the long-ago cause of some deeply embedded fear, and after you have used self-hypnosis and guided imagery a few times, you can easily work out your own suggestions for recalling a long-forgotten scene or fact.

Except for the differences in phrasing suggestions, hypnotic suggestions are virtually identical with those used in guided imagery. Thus you could employ self-hypnosis to use any of the suggestions and imagery described in the remainder of this book.

Don't forget to cancel any temporary suggestions before you return to normal consciousness. For example, if you have suggested that your hand is tingling, or if you have suggested that your hand is as light as a Ping-Pong ball, cancel these suggestions. Otherwise the feeling may persist in the normal state.

For example, tell yourself or have your authority figure tell you: "The tingling has stopped in my hand. My hand feels quite normal again" or "The weightless condition has left your hand. Your hand now feels normal again."

During hypnosis you can give almost any kind of posthypnotic suggestion that you will carry out during normal consciousness. For instance, you might suggest you will wake up promptly at seven o'clock feeling fresh and full of energy. Almost invariably, you will wake exactly at the appointed time, feeling exactly as you suggested you would.

However, most suggestions concerning health improvement or breaking undesirable habits must be repeated a number of times during several, and possibly more, sessions. It often takes some time to reverse a habit or condition you have had for half a lifetime.

Through self-hypnosis you can achieve virtually any health goal that you can program through guided imagery. The difference is a slight one. So take your pick.

11. Guided Imagery: Blueprint for Wellness

THE BACK OF John Duran's neck was peppered with warts. There were sixteen altogether. A dermatologist wanted $50 apiece to remove them. While he was saving up the necessary cash, John came across a book on guided imagery, which was described as one of the most powerful techniques of drugless medicine. John read that by simply making vivid mental pictures of his health goal and reinforcing them with suggestions, he could implant a blueprint for wellness into his whole being and make it materialize. As we think, feel, imagine, and believe, so we become.

John decided to use guided imagery to rid himself of his warts. As he relaxed in the calm state, John made strong, vivid images on his inner movie screen. He pictured his autonomic nervous system causing the smooth muscles to constrict the blood vessels supplying his warts and to cut off their blood supply entirely. Then he pictured armies of white blood cells attacking and destroying the viruses that caused the warts. Last, he pictured his neck unblemished and entirely free of warts. John spent fifteen minutes three times a day on this mental exercise.

For two weeks nothing happened. Then on the sixteenth day three of the warts seemed noticeably smaller. John kept up his daily imagery. By the twenty-fifth day, only three warts remained. As John had imagined, felt, thought, and believed, so he had become. By the thirtieth day, all sixteen warts had completely disappeared.

Guided imagery simply consists of making clear images of what you want to happen. Along with silently worded suggestions, these thought-images make a clear statement to the subconscious of whatever you wish to be. Through regular repetition of the images, you send images of your health goals deeper and deeper into the subconscious. Gradually the subconscious releases powerful inner forces that work subliminally to make your health goals become real.

What actually occurs is that we circumvent the conscious mind, along with all its critical and analytical functions, and we communicate directly with the subconscious. The subconscious uncritically accepts all the thoughts, images, feelings, and beliefs we feed into it. All we need to do is to give the subconscious a clear, vivid picture of the health goals we desire. The subconscious will then motivate the mind-body to make these images real.

Using Your Imagination to Reprogram Your Health

The subconscious communicates through a visual and symbolic language. You cannot order the subconscious to lower your blood pressure by giving a verbal order. You must use symbols in the form of mental pictures along with silent suggestions that heighten your feelings. The imagery and feelings prompt the subconscious to upgrade your health.

The symbols are often extremely simple and direct. For instance, Robert Salada had an irregular heart rate. He was taught to visualize a pendulum swinging at the rate of 65 ticks per minute. After twenty-one fifteen-minute sessions of imagery, Robert's heart rate settled back to normal.

Picture regularly and enthusiastically how you want to become, and you will become what you visualize. What happens, of course, is that the imagery has a profound effect on the autonomic nervous system. The autonomic nervous system controls almost all our involuntary body functions including digestion, blood pressure, heart rate, kidneys, and production of enzymes and hormones. Pain sensations from all over our body feed into the brain along fibers of the autonomic nervous system that parallel blood vessels.

Through guided imagery we can program the autonomic nervous system to change to different nerve pathways or to take up new patterns of behavior: to dilate blood vessels and reduce blood pressure, to constrict blood vessels and relieve headaches, to restrict the blood flow to benign tumors and warts, and to reduce hunger. We can program the autonomic nervous system to raise the pain threshold and to reduce or eliminate pain. No longer need we continue to suffer from dysfunctions caused by the autonomic nervous system that we always considered beyond our control.

Through guided imagery we can also fortify the immune system and increase its aggressiveness in destroying infections and cancer cells. Guided imagery can also help reinforce behavior modification, indirectly raise or lower weight, help break addiction to stimulants, and strengthen our acceptance of new-beliefs. Many pain-clinic personnel consider guided imagery more effective than morphine in reducing pain.

The health-building power of suggestion alone is so great that a 1980 study funded by the National Institutes of Health at the University of California at Davis found that when patients who were undergoing operations were given taped messages with positive suggestions for rapid healing, they recovered significantly sooner than otherwise expected. They needed less pain medication and were out of bed much sooner than other patients who were not given the healing suggestions.

For maximum success, you should prepare your mental pictures and suggestions in advance. Write down exactly what you are trying to heal and, if possible, how your mind-body may accomplish it. Make a rough sketch of each mental picture and write out each suggestion.

How to Make Vivid and Graphic Images

The aim of mental pictures is to show you overcoming your condition or ailment and restoring health. You can use a symbol to visualize your ailment or you can picture it as you imagine it looks. For example, you might visualize staph cells as small, soft, overcooked beans. Or you might visualize a benign tumor as a soft, easily destroyed fungus. Or you could visualize a disease as a scared rabbit or a small, defenseless bird.

You should visualize your ailment only briefly and show it as weak, disoriented, and disorganized. Avoid picturing your ailment as strong, powerful, magical, evil, monstrous, gigantic, or fear-inspiring. This indicates helpless Type C thinking. People who have symbolized their ailment as a lion or tiger, a giant or monster, or a powerful, spreading tree or rock have proved to be fearful of the ailment and to have a low level of confidence and belief in their body's healing power.

By contrast, picture your body's defenses and healing powers as large, strong, powerfully aggressive, invincible, indomitable, and unconquerable. Technique #27 describes how to visualize your immune defense system attacking and destroying infections or cancer cells. Make sketches of your white cells with wolflike fangs and jaws. See them rush at any foreign cell and tear it to shreds. Or you can symbolize your white cells as fierce white dogs or white tigers or as any fierce and aggressive animal that always wins. See the dogs rush in and devour the mushy, overcooked beans that symbolize staph cells. Or picture them tearing to pieces a soft, fragile fungus that symbolizes a benign tumor. Some people have successfully visualized their white cells as fighter planes, tanks, or knights in armor.

Make a rough sketch of yourself in perfect health, free of all pain and disease. Sketch yourself as you were at the healthiest, fittest time of your life. Draw yourself loping easily along a beach, inhaling great quantities of clean air, feeling complete faith in your ability to fight off any infection or ailment. Re-create that feeling of confidence and well-being.

If you have difficulty in doing so, it is probably a sign that you lack belief and confidence in your ability to recover and get well. Like most other alternative therapies, guided imagery can work only if you believe in your body's ability to get well. Imagery won't work if your pictures are clouded with doubts or skepticism or if you insist on proof of how it works or demand a guarantee that you will recover. No doctor can guarantee your recovery either. The holistic approach to healing is pragmatic. If something works, then use it. We don't have to know how or why. Just be satisfied that numerous studies have shown that as long as you cooperate fully, guided imagery can bring into reality any feasible health goal that you suggest and visualize. To help build confidence and enthusiasm, practice technique #1, win-power. Through win-power, you can rapidly build boundless enthusiasm and a burning desire to succeed.

Create clear, strong, vivid, and graphic pictures of your health goals. Not only see yourself running along a beach but feel, hear, smell, taste, and touch the scene. Experience each sensation. Smell the salty tang of drying seaweed, hear the scream of gulls and the roar of surf, feel the sea breeze in your face, the sun on your body, and the grains of sand under your bare feet. Experience how good it feels to be lean, slim, sinewy, and free of pain or fat. Experience the entire scene deeply and vividly. One sense may impress you more than another. You can emphasize this one. Smells, for instance, have tremendous power to re-create vivid images and memories.

Provided our health goals are actually attainable, there is very little that guided imagery cannot accomplish given sufficient time. Very few ailments are not capable of some degree of reversal or improvement, even if they are considered medically incurable. But negative thoughts of doubts or skepticism can seriously mar your chances of success.

INNER HEALING TECHNIQUE #24
Posting Sentinels to Destroy Negative Thoughts

A simple mental technique can destroy all doubts and negative thoughts. You can implant it in your mind any time you are in a deep alpha state and ready for guided imagery.

Visualize two warriors, each armed with a spear. Place one warrior inside each of your frontal lobes or temples. Their task is to watch for a doubt or negative thought and to spear and deflate it as soon as it appears. To test your imagery, place the sentinels on guard. Begin to feed them negative thoughts and doubts. See them hurl their spears into each thought and destroy it. Silently order the sentinels to "remain on guard permanently twenty-four hours a day from now on. Immediately destroy any negative thought or doubt concerning my ability to recover from any ailment and to attain perfect health."

I placed my sentinels on guard seven years ago with instructions to destroy all negative thoughts, groundless fears, and needless doubts. I repeated the visualization half a dozen times. Since then, I cannot recall having had an unjustifiable fear or doubt or a negative thought.

Remember to instruct the sentinels to destroy only groundless and unjustifiable fears and doubts. We still need to experience genuine fears and doubts that might be essential for our safety or survival.

How to Create Strong, Powerful Suggestions

Pattie Kirkland, who was forty pounds overweight, was taught to visualize herself as slim and trim. After a week of visualizing, a compulsive inner voice began urging her to cut out all sugar and fats. The following week, an equally strong inner compulsion urged her to begin taking long daily walks. The urges were so powerful that Pattie felt uncomfortable if she tried to resist. She dropped all fats and sugar from her diet and began walking five miles each day. After only ten weeks, her weight was back to normal.

It is hard to tell exactly what inner forces the imagery triggered. But as in all guided imagery, the suggestions Pattie used played a vital role. As she visualized herself at 125 pounds, Pattie kept repeating phrases like this: "I weigh 125 and I'm wearing a size 10. My weight is perfect. I'm slim, trim, lean, and fit. I feel great and wonderful. I can run, dance, ride a bicycle, and play tennis. I love my new look. I eat only fresh, natural foods. I enjoy long walks and all forms of exercise. I feel terrific and congratulate myself on losing forty pounds."

The role of Pattie's suggestions was not to give orders to her subconscious. The subconscious cannot understand words. Instead, as Pattie made clear, strong pictures of herself minus the forty surplus pounds, she experienced how she would feel when she was slim and healthy. Her suggestions then magnified these feelings. In turn, Pattie's feelings created feedback that intensified her imagery. The purpose of suggestions is to create stronger feelings and stronger images. It is this combination of imagery plus feelings that simulates the subconscious to transform our health goals into reality.

For maximum success, suggestions should always be positive and phrased in the affirmative. Use the pronoun *I* or *we*. Phrase each suggestion in the present tense as though your goal were already accomplished. Instead of saying "I will stop smoking," say "I am a nonsmoker." Instead of "I will stop feeling anxious," say "I am totally free of anxiety." Suppose you weigh 165 pounds. Instead of saying "I will lose forty pounds," say "I am slim and trim and weigh 125 pounds. I feel great."

Use positive action verbs like *I can, I am, I feel,* and *I believe.* Never use words like *try* or *attempt* or *perhaps* or *possibly.* All messages to the subconscious must be absolute.

Since feelings intensify images, tell yourself how it feels to be a nonsmoker, or to be slim and trim, or to have recovered your health. Tell yourself, "I feel wonderful, great, happy, and pleased. I feel really proud that I am now a nonsmoker" or "It feels great to be free of the coffee habit. I feel really pleased and proud of myself." Say this even though you may not have stopped smoking or drinking coffee yet.

Describe the end result and phrase all suggestions as though the desired result had already been achieved: "My gout has disappeared and all stiffness and swelling are gone. My toes and fingers are as flexible and nimble as when I was twenty. I am completely free of pain and I can function perfectly."

All suggestions should be made with eagerness, anticipation, and enthusiasm. Avoid using a hesitant or reticent style. If you prefer, you can simply think your suggestions instead of silently phrasing them. This may heighten results.

Write down your suggestions and pare away excess words until you have only key suggestions left. Keep them short and simple. During guided imagery sessions, repeat each phrase at least four times. As you say it, see it and experience it.

If you have any difficulty making vivid pictures, write out your suggestions several times before you begin each imagery session. Some people do lack vivid imagination, usually because of watching too much TV. People who have difficulty reading may also have poor imagery. If you are in these categories, consider writing out a longer script. In between repetitions of the suggestions, describe the pros and cons of reaching or not reaching your health goals. Also describe obstacles that are preventing you from attaining your health goals. Then either record the script on a cassette tape or memorize it. Eventually your gift of imagery will begin to improve. However, if you have any imagery problem, consider using technique #9, mapping your health goals, as a possible aid.

If you have a serious disease or an urgent condition, schedule three fifteen minute imagery sessions daily. The fifteen minutes begin after you have entered deep relaxation. For less urgent problems, you could schedule only two or even a single session daily. But you will achieve faster results with three daily sessions. A single daily session is adequate for preventive maintenance.

You must believe strongly that your imagery will succeed. But to avoid

134

disappointment, set only realistic goals that you can reasonably expect to attain. If you've lost a finger, no amount of guided imagery is going to grow it back. On the other hand, if you've broken a leg, guided imagery *can* help the bone to mend sooner.

Nor should you expect your recovery to be steady and always perceptible. You may notice no improvement for a month or longer. Then a major recovery step could occur quite suddenly. You might wait another month before a second recovery step occurs. Don't expect improvement on a straight line.

INNER HEALING TECHNIQUE #25
Preparation for Guided Imagery Session

Guided imagery is undertaken during a heightened state of awareness that deepens your ability to concentrate and increases your susceptibility to suggestion.

As a preliminary step to entering guided imagery, you should use steps one, two, and three of the progressive relaxation routine (pages 105-106). At this point, you will be in the calm state with your body deeply relaxed and your mind producing slow alpha brain waves. You will be lying on your back with your eyes closed in a quiet place where you will not be disturbed. Remaining in that relaxed state, visualize yourself standing at the top of a long flight of stairs. The stairs lead down into a garden that surrounds the deep, transparent waters of a spring. Begin walking down the stairs at the rate of about one per second, counting as you go. There are thirty steps to the bottom.

The lowest step brings you next to the deep, translucent spring. The clear water is at least a hundred feet deep. Now toss a shiny, new dime into the spring. Keep your awareness about three feet from the dime as it flashes, twists, darts, and turns on its way to the bottom. Follow it closely all the way to the bottom. All is calm and quiet at the bottom of the spring. The coin rests on the sandy bottom and your mind is in a deep state of peace and serenity.

At this point, you will be in a state of light-to-moderate self-hypnosis and extremely receptive to suggestions of any type.

If you prefer, you can visualize yourself going down in an elevator instead of walking downstairs. Count the floors as they go past: ten, nine, eight, and so on to one, giving yourself about three seconds between floors. The lower you go, the more deeply relaxed you will be.

The more you practice progressive relaxation and visualize walking down the stairs and going down in the spring, the sooner you will be ready for guided imagery. Many people cut their preparation time to three minutes in less than two weeks. To do so, try using technique #16 or #17, then visualize yourself going directly down in the spring. This takes the place of steps one, two, and three of the progressive relaxation method plus the imagery just described.

There is another, faster method. Once you have mastered technique #20 (warming the hands and feet), you can use it to go directly into deep relaxation. As soon as your hands tingle and feel warm, you are in a state of deep relaxation and ready for guided imagery. Using this technique, many people can prepare for guided imagery in just sixty seconds.

Once you are deeply relaxed and ready for imagery, live in the now and keep your awareness on the afflicted body part you wish to heal. You should feel delightfully comfortable with no pain or body sensation but with your mind alert. Then tell yourself: "I can visualize easily and vividly. My mind is open to all healing images and suggestions."

Should any daydream or stray thought wander onto your inner movie screen, slide it aside and continue with your imagery. If distracting thoughts become a problem, the cause may be fear or pain. Ask yourself why these thoughts are intruding. Consider the probable reasons for a few minutes. Then return to your imagery. Often enough, this exercise will stop further distraction.

To work effectively, guided imagery must be entirely effortless. Avoid any hint of striving or intenseness or compulsiveness. Never try to force results. Just go on making pictures and giving suggestions and experiencing the associated feelings. Just let go and enjoy the relaxation, the feelings and the sense of detachment. At all costs, avoid any spirit of grim determination. Relax and let your inner healing powers do the work.

INNER HEALING TECHNIQUE #26
The Seven Stages of Guided Imagery

All the mental pictures and suggestions you are going to use should already have been worked out prior to your first guided imagery session. Know exactly what you are going to do and have the imagery and suggestions ready.

Once your body and mind are relaxed, each fifteen-minute guided imagery session should be divided into seven stages. The approximate time to be spent on each stage is suggested below. This is flexible, of course. Keep your awareness on the afflicted area throughout the time you are visualizing it.

1. Visualize your pain, ailment, or disorder (thirty seconds).

2. Visualize any medical, chiropractic, or other treatment you are receiving

and see it destroying the cause of your illness or pain (seventy-five seconds).

3. Visualize your body's own healing powers destroying the cause of your illness or pain (eight minutes).

4. Visualize the afflicted area as already healed and restored to health (ninety seconds).

5. Visualize yourself in perfect health (seventy-five seconds).

6. Picture your life goals as fulfilled and visualize a good self-image (seventy-five seconds).

7. Congratulate yourself for taking an active part in your own recovery. Tell yourself you are feeling great. Maintain a strongly positive feeling (seventy-five seconds).

Let's review each stage in detail.

1. *Visualize your pain, ailment, or disorder.* Picture it either as you imagine it looks or use a symbol. Visualize all ailments as weak and disoriented. Keep this visualization as brief as possible; the less your mind dwells on the thought of disease, the better. So picture your ailment only long enough to grasp what the problem is and where it is located.

2. *Visualize any medical, chiropractic, or other treatment you are receiving and see it destroying the cause of your illness or pain.* If you are taking medication, picture it as a green fluid if it soothes or as an orange fluid if it attacks and destroys foreign cells or viruses. Visualize the medication succeeding at whatever it is supposed to do. If it's a soothing balm, see a green fluid soothing a raw area and restoring it to a normal, healthy pink. If your medication is an antibiotic, see it as an orange fluid that envelops the invading bacteria and burns them away. Picture the diseased area shrinking while healthy cells remain untouched. See the foreign cells or viruses or the diseased area as weak and easily destroyed.

Guided imagery is not a substitute for necessary medical treatment. Although terminal cancer has been reportedly reversed by guided imagery alone, I recommend that you consult a physician or oncologist for diagnosis and advice. Guided imagery will not replace exercise and diet in reversing heart disease, nor will it mend a broken bone. But it will strongly reinforce all types of therapy by visualizing the therapy succeeding and by motivating you to stay with the treatment and persevere. Studies have shown that guided imagery can significantly speed up recovery time and reinforce the effectiveness of the treatment itself.

If you are undergoing chiropractic or any kind of alternative therapy, visualize that succeeding also. If you are taking radiation treatment, picture

137

that as destroying the weak cancer cells and leaving your own body's strong, healthy cells intact. If you are taking nutritional supplements, visualize the vitamins and minerals being carried by your bloodstream to the afflicted area where they rejuvenate ailing tissue and organs.

Reserve top place in your healing priorities to the body's own recuperative powers. Certainly you should visualize any kind of treatment succeeding, but always bear in mind that it is your own body's healing powers that really count.

Maintain a friendly feeling toward all medical treatment, personnel, drugs, and technology. If you experience any hostility, direct it toward the real enemy—your ailment or pain.

If you are not taking any kind of treatment, distribute the seventy-five seconds allotted to stage 2 among the other stages.

3. *Visualize your body's own healing powers destroying the cause of your illness or pain.* This is the principal stage. Here you should spend eight full minutes repeatedly visualizing your body's healing powers attacking and destroying foreign cells or tumors, ulcers, warts, or sores. Symbols are just as effective in the visualization process. For instance, you can picture your body's white cells as fierce dogs, soldiers, tanks, or warriors. Several standard imagery and suggestion routines are described in chapter 13 for use with specific common ailments. Technique #20 and technique #27 can be used in stage 3.

For less common ailments, there is no standard programming. If possible, have your doctor explain what steps the body's healing powers should take to reverse any specific condition or consult a medical encyclopedia. Then simply design your own imagery and suggestions to structure a personal program you feel will work for you. Don't hesitate to revise any program to meet changing conditions.

Some healing processes you can visualize are swollen areas and organs shrinking back to normal size; inflammation flowing out of swollen joints; pus draining from infected areas; damaged or swollen tissue becoming soothed; energy flowing to tired or afflicted areas; hot, feverish areas becoming cool; crippled joints becoming flexible; and tense areas relaxing. If you suffer from insomnia, picture yourself sleeping soundly each night.

What you are experiencing here is inner healing in action. Picture the body's own recuperative and rejuvenative powers destroying disease or eliminating a disorder and restoring high-level wellness. As you think, feel, imagine, and believe, so you become.

4. *Visualize the afflicted area as already healed and restored to health.* Do as John Duran did. He visualized his neck smooth and unblemished, free of the sixteen disfiguring warts. Whatever disorder or ailment you have, picture it gone and your body restored to perfect health.

For an inner condition like hypertension, you may have to use symbolism. But in most cases, you can visualize the actual ailment disappearing.

Picture any diseased area as healthfully pink and free of all swelling, pain, or sign of disorder. See it as it was before the ailment occurred. Imagine it as smooth, moist, warm, comfortable, at ease, youthful, resilient, supple, and flexible—or whatever best portrays a condition of perfect health.

This is an important goal picture. So make it strong, clear, vivid, and graphic.

5. *Visualize yourself in perfect health.* Picture your whole person as radiantly healthy. Recall how you looked and felt at the healthiest and fittest period in your life. Experience how easily and effortlessly you moved, how calm, content, satisfied, loving, and fulfilled you felt. Recall how good you felt about life in general and about your self-image in particular.

Picture yourself in the same superhealthy state, loping easily along a beach, completely in harmony with nature, knowing that your body can fight off every kind of human ailment. See yourself as lean, fit, suntanned, and athletic.

Then realize that just below the thin veneer of symptoms that mask your wellness lie the same superhealth and wonderful well-being that you once enjoyed. In most cases, all you need to do to restore it is to stop abusing your body with toxins and atrophy and your mind with outdated beliefs and to allow your own recuperative powers to go to work to rejuvenate your whole person.

When you visualize your self-image, you will probably want to use the suggestions in chapter 7.

6. *Picture your life goals as fulfilled and visualize a good self-image.* Visualize your self-image or your self-image symbol (a calm, loving bicyclist or cross-country skier or a brook or a dog). Experience genuine liking and love for what you see. For a few seconds, feel a very strong love for yourself. Feel that you are beautiful and OK.

Your self-image is largely composed of your life goals. Select your most important goal and picture yourself having already achieved it. For example, if you dream of owning an ocean-going sailboat, picture yourself at the helm of your own cruising ketch. Feel the tiller straining against your hand as you hold the ship on a broad reach. Hear the creak of sheets and rigging as the ship forges ahead with a fine bone of white water under her bow. See yourself taking a couple of years off and sailing around the world.

The idea is to visualize a very strong reason for becoming well. Full details for building a strong self-image and for choosing quality goals are described in chapter 7.

7. *Congratulate yourself for taking an active role in your own recovery.* Repeat the classic suggestion: "Every day in every way I am getting better and better." As you say it, feel yourself well, cheerful, optimistic, and full of renewed energy.

Then continue, "On the reverse count of five, I will return to normal consciousness. As I do, I feel health, comfort, love, calm, and happiness radiating all over me. These and other new-belief qualities will stay with me and become a permanent part of my personality. Five, four, three, two, one."

The more frequently you practice guided imagery, the more effective it becomes.

12. Seven Holistic Steps to High-Level Wellness

REGARDLESS OF HOW effectively you use your mind to heal your body, you can multiply the results of your mind's healing power by using it holistically. That means using your self-healing powers on the physical, mental, and emotional levels simultaneously. Remember the wellness equation:

Diet + Exercise + Positive Thinking = High-Level Wellness.

Positive thinking is most effective when used in conjunction with a healthful diet, exercise, and other good health habits. For optimum results, we should boost inner healing with sound nutrition and abundant daily exercise. We should cut out all health-destroying lifestyle risks and replace them with health-building habits. Regardless of how faithfully or how well people practice guided imagery, if they continue to indulge in such self-destructive habits as smoking, overeating, a high-fat diet, or heavy coffee or alcohol drinking, they will hinder their inner healing powers in restoring health. People with poor health habits are generally cancer-prone Type C personalities.

By contrast, people who eliminate all lifestyle health risks and replace them with good health habits can double or triple the effects of their inner healing powers. By doing so, they are automatically creating positive self-images and transforming themselves into disease-resistant Type B personalities.

The following steps combined with inner healing techniques produce a well-rounded, complete holistic program.

The Seven Holistic Steps to High-Level Wellness

1. Cease taking all unnecessary drugs and medications.

2. Exercise regularly and abundantly every day.

3. Eat a low-fat diet of natural, high-fiber foods.

4. Eat sparingly and only when hungry.

5. Cut out stimulants.

6. Stop smoking.

7. Give the body its natural biological requirements.

The attainment of each of these steps could become a short-term goal that you could use in building a strong self-image (see chapter 7). Through practicing the inner healing methods in this book, you are already on your way to transforming most positive stress into negative stress, overlaying negative emotions with positive emotions, replacing unhealthy, outdated beliefs with new-beliefs, changing all primitive expectations into rather-beliefs, and creating a strong, positive self-image. You are well on the way to becoming a Type B personality with clear and well-defined goals.

You'll find guided imagery tremendously helpful in motivating you as you begin to practice the seven holistic steps. For instance, imagery can help you stop smoking, improve your nutrition, or lose weight. If you already have a degenerative disease, such as an ulcer, it may be more urgent to concentrate your imagery sessions on visualizing the ulcer being healed. If you are obese and have cancer, it is probably more urgent to reserve your imagery sessions for technique #27 (programming your immune system to destroy infections and cancer).

So, depending on your priorities, you may have to put the seven holistic steps into effect without the help of guided imagery. However, you still have the entire range of inner healing techniques to help you, especially such powerful aids as win-power, the sudden-stop method, deep breathing, and the various physical relaxation methods.

A closer look at the seven steps will give you a good idea of how they can reinforce the inner healing techniques.

1. *Cease taking all unnecessary drugs and medications.* All drugs and medications are toxic and have side effects that can damage your health. The first step toward regaining wellness is to throw out all unnecessary drugs and medications. Continue to take only essential drugs prescribed by your physician but ask your doctor to phase them out as soon as possible. If you are on maintenance drugs, reduce the dosage only under medical supervision. If your doctor is not prevention-oriented, you should change to a doctor who is aware that drugs and surgery are not the only ways to get well. Avoid using common over-the-counter medications. Salves or medications for external use only are considered safe.

2. *Exercise regularly and abundantly every day.* Very gradually, without ever becoming tired or fatigued, work up to walking five brisk miles each day. Alternatively, an equivalent amount of any other continuous rhythmic exercise such as jogging, swimming, aerobic dancing, or bicycling is equally beneficial. A brisk five-mile walk or its equivalent will reduce anxiety, tension, or depression more effectively than any tranquilizer. It will lower blood pressure, reduce cholesterol levels, strengthen the heart, lungs, and every muscle in the body, eliminate chronic fatigue, and help shed surplus pounds. It is also helpful if you are giving up smoking.

Most people can begin an easy walking program without requiring a medical checkup. But if you are over thirty-five, obese, on medication, a heavy drinker or smoker, or unable to walk a mile in seventeen or eighteen minutes, or if you have had, or suspect you may have, any form of heart trouble, hypertension, or any degenerative or other disease, you should check with your doctor before beginning an exercise program. Make sure, when you consult a physician, that he or she favors exercise. Otherwise, you are wasting your time and money. For most Americans, the dangers of not exercising are at least a hundred times greater than any risks incurred by exercise. So consult a doctor who you know is a jogger, runner, or exercise buff.

There is no such thing as being too old to exercise. Dr. Herbert De Vries, director of exercise physiology at Andrus Gerontology Center at the University of Southern California, found that when older people take up a structured exercise program, many symptoms of pain, anger, and poor health disappear. Many gerontologists recommend that we should take more exercise after age fifty, not less.

If you are out of shape, ease into exercise very, very gradually. Your pulse will warn you if you're overdoing it. After exercising, rest one full minute. If your pulse exceeds 130 beats per minute, you are overdoing it. Reduce your speed and distance, and take your pulse five minutes after exercising. It should read 120 or less. Ten minutes after exercising, it should read 100 or less. Other warning signs are a pain or tightness in the chest with severe breathlessness, lightheadedness, dizziness, nausea, or loss of muscle control. If any of these occurs, stop immediately and see a doctor.

Once you can walk five brisk miles each day, you can begin to jog or to alternate with other kinds of aerobic exercise. A brisk five-mile daily walk is one of the most effective ways to lose weight permanently. Diet alone seldom achieves permanent weight loss because it is not holistic.

Use guided imagery to picture yourself as an accomplished walker—lean, fit, and tireless. Visualize yourself enjoying your walk as the high spot of each day. Experience the inspiration and the wonderful feeling of well-being that walking produces. See yourself spurning TV or other sedentary pastimes in favor of walking. Picture yourself walking everywhere. Consider planning a goal in which you spend an entire vacation walking.

3. *Eat a low-fat diet of natural high-fiber foods.* Most quick weight-loss diets are nutritionally unsound and are often dangerously high in fat and animal protein. You may lose weight for a while but your cholesterol level will soar. And because the diet is monotonous and unholistic, you will find it intolerable. The only way to lose weight permanently is to combine regular daily exercise with a low-fat diet of natural high-fiber foods—and to continue both for the rest of your life.

The healthiest diet for humans is the 80-10-10 diet, in which 80 percent of calories is derived from complex, unrefined carbohydrates (fresh fruits, vegetables, and whole grains); a maximum of 10 percent is derived from fat (ideally obtained from fresh nuts, seeds, or avocados); and not more than 10 percent is derived from protein (preferably from vegetarian sources like beans, nuts, and seeds or from very low-fat dairy foods, fish, or poultry without the skin).

On this basis, the following gremlin foods should be totally excluded from the diet: saturated fats, hydrogenated vegetable oils, all fried foods, all fatty foods, poultry skin, all regular dairy foods and milk; all processed, prepared, and canned foods; all salt and commercial sauces, ketchup, mayonnaise, and condiments; bacon, egg yolks, ham, lard, luncheon meat, organ meats, pork, prime beef, processed cheese, sausages, seafood, shellfish, shortening, smoked meats, snack foods, frozen dinners; cakes, candy, baked goods; refined rice, refined pasta, refined flour, and all sugar; jams, jellies, pies, and pastries; all types of sweeteners; and white or imitation whole-grain bread (any bread not labeled "100 percent whole grain" is imitation whole-grain bread).

Sugar, whether refined or unrefined, is a high-risk food that has been linked with almost every degenerative disease. It is found in almost every canned and processed food from baked beans to sauces, pickles, chow mein, carbonated beverages, and children's breakfast cereals.

All of these high-risk foods are low in fiber. Numerous studies have shown that natural high-fiber foods like fresh vegetables, fruits, and whole grains can prevent, or even help reverse, many degenerative diseases including adult-onset diabetes, heart disease, hypertension, atherosclerosis and diverticulosis. In contradiction to the myths that are perpetually repeated in most diet books, you will not gain weight by eating potatoes, carrots, turnips, or other natural, unprocessed starchy foods. It's not the potato that makes people fat; but the cream, butter, and other gremlin foods we put on the potato are fattening. A baked potato contains only 100 calories but a fried potato contains 500!

Eat as much raw food as possible. Use natural herbs for seasoning and dressings. A high-fiber 80-10-10 diet helps prevent constipation, varicose veins, hemorrhoids, dental cavities, gallstones, and colonic cancer. In conjunction with positive thinking and daily exercise, it provides almost total immunity from cardiovascular disease and cancer.

If changing over to the 80-10-10 diet seems rather drastic, try the following transition diet. Before eating your usual breakfast, eat four pieces of fresh fruit such as an apple, a pear, a banana, and a slice of melon. Then, if you still feel hungry, you can begin to eat your regular breakfast.

Before eating your usual lunch, eat a large, fresh vegetable salad. Not until you have eaten all the salad will you permit yourself to begin eating your regular lunch, and then only if you are still hungry. Apply the same rule at dinner. Soon you will find yourself so enjoying the fruits and salads that you will phase out all the gremlin foods.

Use guided imagery to visualize yourself enjoying a delicious succulent fruit or vegetable salad. See yourself facing a greasy plate of ham and eggs and feeling repelled and nauseated. Picture yourself throwing out every type of gremlin food in your kitchen and feeding it to hogs. See yourself freed from greasy dishes and long hours of cooking over a hot stove. Picture yourself at your ideal weight and realize that you achieved it through eschewing fat and sugar and by eating only natural, high-fiber foods—and, of course, by walking five brisk miles each day.

A reminder: No food of animal origin (including poultry, fish, eggs, and dairy foods) contains any appreciable fiber. Fiber occurs only in vegetarian foods, particularly in whole grains.

4. *Eat sparingly and only when hungry.*   Overeating can be as dangerous to the heart and arteries as a high-fat diet. Nutritionists including Nathan Pritikin and Dr. Allen B. Nicholls of the University of Montreal have discovered that risk of heart attack, hypertension, atherosclerosis, and diabetes can be significantly reduced by dividing each standard-sized meal into two or three mini-meals and eating a mini-meal every ninety minutes or so throughout the day.

By eating six to nine mini-meals daily—based on the 80-10-10 diet, of course—it's impossible to stuff yourself or overeat or to have digestive problems or feel logy after a meal.

You can easily eat a mini-meal at breakfast, another at mid-morning, one for lunch, one in mid-afternoon, another at five o'clock, and two or three more during the evening. You should, of course, eat only when you are hungry.

You can easily visualize yourself breaking up each standard-sized meal into mini-meals. During imagery, experience how good it is to always feel light and free of digestive burdens.

5. *Cut out stimulants.* Guided imagery is the best way to program your entire organism to drop the caffeine habit. A moderate alcohol addiction may also be deprogrammed the same way. Visualize yourself as a total abstainer from caffeine-containing drinks (black tea, coffee, cola drinks) and alcohol. See yourself beginning a totally new life as a nondrinker of caffeine and alcohol. Picture yourself feeling repelled whenever anyone offers you a drink containing caffeine or alcohol. Experience how good it feels to break your dependence on these stimulants. Picture your heart beating more strongly, your arteries dilated, and your blood pressure low.

If you experience any urge to take a stimulant, use the sudden-stop method (technique #2) to rid yourself of the negative thought that is urging you to feel you need caffeine or alcohol. Also use win-power (technique #1) to resist giving in to the urge.

You can help ease yourself out of the coffee habit by substituting tea. Black tea contains only half as much caffeine per cup as coffee. If you habitually drink six cups of coffee a day, replace one cup of coffee per day with a cup of tea. After six days, you will be drinking only tea and your caffeine intake will be cut in half. Then, each day, replace one cup of black tea with a cup of herb tea, carob, or diluted fruit juice. In six more days, you'll be off the caffeine habit altogether.

Guided imagery can motivate you to make this gradual changeover. Picture yourself already free of the caffeine addiction. One imagery session per day should be sufficient to break the caffeine habit. It may take three daily sessions to break a moderate addiction to alcohol.

6. *Stop smoking.* No cigarette smoker can achieve high-level wellness or really love himself or herself. Smoking cigarettes is a suicidal habit that automatically brands a person with a Type C personality. Yet millions of adult Americans *have* quit smoking successfully, many after twenty or thirty years on the drug. It takes only five days of abstinence to break physical dependence on nicotine.

While government researchers report that quitting cold turkey is easiest for most people, I believe that inner healing techniques plus the "five-minute plan" offer an even more certain and less painful method.

The five-minute plan is based on adding five minutes to each interval between cigarettes. You begin with a one-hour interval. Your next cigarette is due one hour and five minutes later. The next is due one hour and ten minutes later. Each interval becomes five minutes longer than the previous interval. No cigarettes are permitted one hour before bedtime, after rising, or for one hour after any meal (based on a three-meals-a-day routine).

Whenever you feel like smoking a cigarette, take a glass of fruit juice or any other beverage you enjoy (but not coffee or alcohol). You may chew gum, hard candy, fruit cake, dried fruits, or do virtually anything else to take the place of cigarettes during the first two weeks. Exercise like walking, swimming, canoeing, or bicycling is one of the best substitutes for smoking.

The five-minute plan permits a relatively painless and gradual withdrawal from nicotine over a five-day period. During the following five days, you break all physical dependence on nicotine. After that, inner healing techniques will save you from giving in whenever stress or negative emotions create the urge for a cigarette.

Set a date to begin the five-minute plan, starting within one week. It may be best to begin on a Friday so that you have the second and third days at home away from job stress. Begin now to use progressive relaxation and guided imagery three times a day. Visualize yourself as a nonsmoker, starting out on a wonderful new adventure of cigarette-free living. Imagine yourself able to taste and smell again. Picture yourself walking or jogging through a park while you inhale the rich fragrance of grass, hay, and flowers. See yourself sitting down to a vegetable salad served without a dressing and enjoy the rich taste nuances of the vegetables themselves. Picture your breath as fresh as a baby's, your teeth free of tobacco stain, and your tongue pink and free of yellow nicotine film. See your lungs changing from tar-blackened, cancer-prone air sacs into healthy, pink organs. Visualize yourself starting out on an exciting journey to high-level wellness in which you will feel good and be happy all of the time.

Start the five-minute plan with a bout of technique #1 (win-power) as soon as you awaken. Use self-remembering (technique #3) to remind yourself that win-power is yours to turn on at any time. Be prepared to use the sudden-stop method whenever a thought of smoking intrudes. Slide the negative thought off your inner movie screen and replace it with a positive thought that you are a nonsmoker.

While using the five-minute plan, you are allowed to smoke one cigarette at the permissible intervals. You'll find it even easier to kick the habit if you smoke the brand that you least enjoy.

If you have not eliminated stress by reprogramming your belief system, practice removing tension by tensing your muscles using technique #14 or #15. Follow this with technique #11 (deep breathing). Technique #19, rapid relaxation response, is another dependable way to prevent getting uptight and reaching for a cigarette.

If you do feel a strong urge to smoke, use techniques #1, #15, and #11 immediately. Win-power followed by muscle tensing and deep breathing provides a powerful defense against any inclination to light up.

Read chapter 7 and create a good self-image around seeing yourself as a nonsmoker. Plan goals that assume you have become a nonsmoker for life. Visualize yourself becoming a distance swimmer, walker, or bicyclist. See yourself walking briskly up mountains. Imagine yourself able to draw in huge gulps of fresh country and mountain air.

Maintain imagery sessions three times a day until you have been off cigarettes for at least seven days. Maintain two sessions daily for another week. After that, a single session daily for the following week should see you safely off cigarettes for life.

If you haven't already done so, study chapters 3 through 6 and update your beliefs to eliminate stress. Most people who weaken and go back to smoking do so in the belief that cigarettes will help relieve their stress. Any relief, of course, is temporary. Over the long pull, cigarettes only intensify stress.

For any cigarette smoker, stopping smoking is the greatest single step he or she can make toward attaining lifelong health and happiness.

7. *Give the body its natural biological requirements.* To attain total wellness, we need pure air and water, sunshine, security, a quiet environment, and adequate rest and sleep. Although not everyone needs seven to eight hours of sleep, you should allow yourself all the sleep you require. If you have trouble getting to sleep, or if you lie awake during the night, inner healing techniques can probably help.

Use technique #11 (deep breathing), followed by technique #12 (mental relaxation). If these don't get you to sleep, go on to technique #18 (combined deep breathing and relaxation counting). Then continue with technique #20 (warming the hands and feet).

If even that doesn't put you to sleep, get up and go to another room and stay there until you do feel sleepy. If you're troubled by chronic sleeplessness, begin to get up an hour earlier and spend the extra hour walking. In a few days, you should be sleeping soundly.

13. *Healing Visualizations for Guided Imagery*

THIS CHAPTER gives basic suggestions for using your mind and thoughts to reverse some common human ailments. The following are suggested guided imagery visualizations for healing common degenerative and infectious diseases. The first four are inner healing techniques that are applicable to a variety of ailments; the remainder are designed for specific ailments. The basis of these techniques is technique #26, and the stage referred to in these techniques are the seven stages of guided imagery (see chapter 11).

INNER HEALING TECHNIQUE #27
Programming Your Immune System to Destroy Infections and Cancer

Through imagery, we can ask the subconscious to strengthen the body's defenses against cancer cells or against infections such as invading bacteria or viruses. Regardless of the type of disease cell or virus we want destroyed, the method is the same. To perform this technique successfully, you should have read and absorbed chapters 1 and 2. Although this technique is not a substitute for necessary medical treatment, its use as a cancer therapy is growing rapidly.

In this technique, always visualize disease cells individually, not in large colonies or in a mass forming a tumor. Picture viruses as small, individual cells that have only a nucleus.

Cancer cells, or neoplastic cells (as physicians call them), are ordinary body cells that contain mutated genetic coding. This alters their antigen so that the white cells of our immune system recognize them, along with other disease cells, as foreign. The immune system then rallies to attack and destroy all cells that it recognizes as foreign (this is more fully described in chapter 2).

149

Malignant cells become immortal. They clone and form a tumor. When a tumor becomes large, or during a biopsy, cancer cells may break loose and spread elsewhere in the body to clone again and form another tumor. Cancer cells can survive only when a person's immune system is weak or suppressed, which is why only one person in five ever gets cancer.

Through imagery and suggestion, we can urge the subconscious to revitalize the immune system so that it can overpower disease cells.

Begin with a brief stage 1 visualization of the disease site. Visualize the disease cells as small, weak, confused, disoriented, soft, frightened, and easily destroyed gray cells. Picture a dozen or eighteen at most. See them outnumbered a hundred to one by large, aggressive white cells thirsting for battle.

In your stage 3 visualization, see your white cells as fierce and aggressive with wolflike jaws and fangs ready to savagely attack and tear to shreds any disease cell. You can symbolize your white cells as fierce white hunting dogs or as sharks or piranhas or eagles or any kind of predator. Or you can picture them as knights or soldiers or as fighter planes. Visualize them as vicious and angry, without a hint of mercy or gentleness. Picture your white cells as powerful, destructive, conquering, and bursting with energy. As soon as they spot a disease cell, your white cells rush at it and triumphantly tear it into small pieces. The number of white cells is unlimited. You have billions in reserve. You can't lose.

After a few successful attacks, get into the picture yourself. See yourself as a white knight or soldier armed with a sword and lead an attack. Vent all your hate and hostility on the disease cells. Hack them to pieces with your sword. Stab them. Tear them. Crush them underfoot. Then order your white cells or hunting dogs to carry away the remains and flush them out through your kidneys.

Don't permit a single disease cell to survive. Keep repeating this visualization for the full eight minutes allotted to stage 3.

Some therapists prefer that patients think their suggestions during immune-system imagery rather than saying the suggestions quietly. Or you can use phrases like these: "My white cells are angry and fierce. They are thirsting to kill and destroy disease cells. The disease cells in my body are small, few, weak, and confused. As I give the order to 'charge,' my white cells attack and destroy the disease cells. They are tearing the disease cells to pieces. My white cells are attacking in packs. Now I lead a pack in the attack. My sword goes right through a disease cell. I hack and cut and twist and slash it. I hate the disease cells. I am so angry with the disease that I crush the remains of the cell under my heel. All the disease cells are dead. My white cells are carrying away the remains."

Imagery will help overcome any infection that the immune system is capable of destroying, including cancer. It should be used along with, not as a substitute for, necessary medical care. Even with a simple staph infection or boil, you should still use physical therapy such as hot compresses to dilate the blood vessels and make it easier for white cells to reach the infection.

INNER HEALING TECHNIQUE #28
Strangling a Benign Tumor or Wart

In this technique you visualize the artery supplying blood to the benign tumor or wart you wish to eliminate. Picture the nerve fibers running the length of the artery. Also visualize the smooth muscles that surround the artery constricting it and reducing the blood flow through it. As you give the command, picture the nerves triggering the muscles to squeeze and constrict the artery. In just a brief time, the vasoconstrictor muscles have shut off the blood supply to the wart or tumor. Without blood, the wart or tumor is starved of oxygen and nutrients. The wart or tumor wilts and shrinks and in a short time disappears.

Use this imagery only on a benign tumor. Employ technique #27 for malignant tumors. For warts, which are caused by a virus, use both this technique and technique #27. Allot four minutes to visualizing each technique.

Use appropriate phrases as you visualize: "My muscles are constricting the artery and cutting off the blood supply to the tumor. Now the tumor is completely starved of oxygen and nutrients. The tumor cells are dying. Now all the tumor cells are dead. The tumor is shrinking. The tumor has completely disappeared."

INNER HEALING TECHNIQUE #29
Relieving Chronic Pain

Pain clinics make greater use of deep relaxation and guided imagery than of any other therapy. During recent years, scientists have discovered that when the body enters the calm state—with an alpha or theta brain-wave frequency and with the entire organism deeply relaxed—the body releases pain-killing endorphine that acts like novocaine on pain receptors in the spine and brain. Pain is blocked out and the pain threshold rises dramatically.

Pain and anxiety often coexist. As you recall, anxiety cannot exist without muscle tension. So when we voluntarily use a muscle-tensing exercise (such as technique #11, #14, #15, or #16) to eliminate tension, anxiety is forced out of the mind, and along with it goes much of our pain.

151

The first step in reducing chronic pain is to use progressive relaxation to enter the calm state. At this point, you may also invite your intuitive guide (technique #22) to investigate the cause of the pain and to make suggestions for relieving it. Ask your intuitive guide why you have the pain, what purpose it serves, and whether the pain is trying to tell you something. Within a day or so, you may receive the answer in the form of a dream or intuition or inner voice.

If you have sore ligaments, for example, have your intuitive guide give these ligaments an inner massage. It may be all in your imagination, but the effects can be surprisingly real.

Many pain-relieving techniques are based on imagery and suggestion. Following is a brief review of those most popular with pain clinic therapists. You must be in the calm alpha state and deeply relaxed to practice any of the following techniques. Use whichever one seems most appropriate.

What does the pain feel like? Place your awareness on the painful area and ask yourself where the pain is, what kind of pain it is (steady or pulsating), and what it feels like. If the pain feels like a spike driven through your knee, ask yourself what would soothe it. Most likely, you'd answer: a block of ice. These symbols should be used in imagery as soon as you think of them.

So imagine your knee with a spike driven through it. Very slowly, a fraction of an inch at a time, picture the spike being eased out of your knee. This action should take about two minutes. As the spike finally comes out, feel the pain disappear. Then see your knee completely encased in a block of ice. Within seconds, your knee is so numb that you cannot feel pain.

As you visualize the scene, repeat phrases like: "As the spike comes out, the pain vanishes. My knee feels numb. My knee is comfortable and free of pain. Every day in every way my knee is getting better and better. I feel perfectly comfortable. The pain is gone."

You can use this same theme in many ways. For instance, your knee might have felt as though it were on fire with pain. In this case, you might have plunged it into cold water instead of encasing it in ice. Your spine might feel as if it were tied in knots. Or your backbone might feel as though it were studded with nails. Here again, as you slowly untie the knot or pull out the nails, you'd feel the pain disappear altogether. Bursitis in the shoulder might feel like a sword driven through your shoulder blade. Visualize the sword being slowly withdrawn and then soothe it.

Fill the pain with water. Focus your awareness on the painful area and analyze its exact shape, size, and color. Then estimate how much water would be required to fill the area. Frequently, this exercise alone significantly reduces the pain. So repeat the exercise several times.

If pain still remains, picture the painful area filled with ice-cold water. Feel the cold water numbing the pain and bringing comfort. As you visualize all this, repeat phrases like: "The ice-cold water has numbed my pain. My pain is completely gone. I feel perfectly comfortable and free of pain."

Switching off pain. Picture the nerve fiber leading from the painful area to the pain receptor in the brain. Just before the fiber enters the brain visualize a pain-gate symbolized by a switch. See yourself turning off this switch. As you do, the pain ends. Since this is a brief exercise, repeat it a number of times. Eventually, the subconscious will turn off your pain-gate switch just as you visualized.

Detach the pain from your body. Visualize the painful area completely detached from your body. For instance, if your right shoulder is painful, visualize your right arm severed at the shoulder. See your right arm floating off in space. Anyone capable of vivid, graphic imagery can usually reduce pain significantly by this method.

Diffuse the pain. If your pain is localized in a small area, visualize it diffusing and spreading out all over your body. As it does, the intensity is also diluted and spread out, and you do not feel the pain as intensely as in the original site. Next, visualize the pain leaving the body through the skin. Repeated several times, this technique can be surprisingly effective.

Projecting your pain away. Place your awareness on your pain and visualize its shape, size, and color. Then, in your imagination, project the painful area out into space about twelve feet in front of you. Next, enlarge the painful area to ten times its original size and area. Then shrink it down to the size of a marble. Enlarge it again to its original size. Magnify and reduce its size again several times. Finally, fill the painful area with a bright green light. While it is still filled with green light, return the painful area back to your body.

In most cases, the simple distraction of doing this exercise makes you forget all about the pain and the pain has vanished by the time you finish the exercise.

Fill the pain with sunshine. Fill the painful area with a bright burst of imaginary sunshine. For instance, if your knee is painful, picture the whole knee flooded with bright sunshine. Feel the knee becoming heavy and warm. As you do, repeat such phrases as: "My knee is heavy and warm. My knee is completely relaxed. The pain is gone. My knee feels perfectly comfortable."

INNER HEALING TECHNIQUE #30
Healing with Sunshine

Most imagery therapists believe that visualizing radiant sunshine is one of the most powerful therapeutic devices. To do so, you simply picture the afflicted area bathed in brilliant sunshine.

This is one of the best ways to help heal a nerve. If a nerve in your right thigh is afflicted or painful, picture the entire spinal area bathed in brilliant sunshine. Run a flare of sunlight down the nerve fibers on the right side of the spine and follow the nerve paths down into your thigh. Picture all the nerves in the thigh glowing with sunlight. Feel the warm healing power of the sun radiating through every nerve and all over your thigh.

Since the sun symbolizes the healing energy of our life force and will to live, you can use it liberally to suffuse any painful or afflicted area. You can enhance your own life force and will to live by imagining your entire body bathed in golden sunshine. Inhale slow, deep breaths of imaginary sunshine. Feel the warm energy-charged sunshine filling your lungs and spreading throughout your body. Tell yourself you are drawing in new life force with each breath.

If you have a diseased or afflicted area, for example a bladder, picture it bathed in healing sunlight. Feel the warmth radiating through the bladder, making it heavy and pleasurable. Use phrases such as: "My bladder feels heavy and warm. Every day in every way my bladder is getting better and better. As new life energy flows into my bladder, I feel my bladder becoming more comfortable and stronger and healthier. My bladder is already in perfect health."

Feel the sunshine circulating through the afflicted area, soothing it and making it heavy and warm. This imagery will help dilate the blood vessels and bring more oxygen, nutrients, and white cells to the area. Sunshine can be beneficially used in conjunction with almost any other type of visualization. Naturally, however, this technique should not be used on a benign tumor (use technique #28 instead).

Another variation of this exercise is to breathe deeply and slowly. As you do, visualize a wave of sunlight flowing in through your feet and up the front of your entire body, filling the legs, trunk, arms, and head. This warm, pleasurable wave of sunshine relaxes and recharges the whole body. As you exhale, see the same wave of sunshine flowing down the back of your body and out through the legs.

INNER HEALING TECHNIQUE #31
Inner Healing for Common Diseases

The following are visualization exercises for healing specific diseases. Again, the basis for these exercises is technique #26, the seven stages of guided imagery.

Inner Healing for Arthritis and Gout

For simple relief from the pain of osteoarthritis, rheumatoid arthritis, or gout, use the visualizations recommended in technique #29. Warming the hands and feet (technique #20) has also been found beneficial.

Although osteoarthritis, rheumatoid arthritis, and gout are all worsened by emotional stress and destructive lifestyle risks, each has a different pathogenesis and requires a different imagery.

Adult rheumatoid arthritis appears as an inflammation of the joints and joint linings, usually in the fingers, toes, wrists, ankles, and knees. It is most common between ages twenty and forty-five and it strikes three times as many women as men. The latest research is confirmng that rheumatoid arthritis is caused by a food allergy that triggers the same immune response as would an infectious disease. The white blood cell (lymphocyte) count rises rapidly as the body manufactures armies of lymphocytes to deal with an invader. But the only invaders are tiny portions of allergenic food.

When there are no foreign cells or virus to attack, lymphocytes are bio- logically programmed to destroy the body's own weak, diseased, or degenerated tissue. Since our joints undergo more stress than other skeletal areas, a joint may become di-stressed through injury, overuse, or poor nutrition. Any such di-stressed joint becomes an immediate target for harassment by hordes of surplus lymphocytes. Inflammation, pain, and swelling are the body's healing response to this autoimmune attack.

Rheumatoid arthritis lasts as long as we continue to eat gremlin foods that our immune system in unable to tolerate. Flare-ups with crippling pain almost always follow a binge of eating any of the health-destroying foods listed in holistic step 3 on page 144. Flare-ups are also often precipitated by stress.

Rheumatoid arthritis is considered medically incurable. All anti-arthritic drugs have severe side effects and none does more than alleviate symp- toms. Rheumatoid arthritis can be reversed only by removing the cause— our suicidal habits of eating, living, and thinking. The role of guided imagery is to motivate us to drop all life-threatening habits and to replace them with the seven holistic steps to wellness described in Chapter 12.

Begin by visualizing yourself following holistic step 3. Then gradually work the other steps into your imagery. As you put step 3 and the other steps into actual practice, the pain and inflammation of rheumatoid arthritis should gradually disappear. Your success hinges on eliminating virtually all emotional stress and all but the completely natural, high-fiber foods recom- mended in holistic step 3.

A word about exercise (holistic step 2): If you have rheumatoid arthritis, consider starting out with such gentle exercises as yoga or tai-chi rather than anything more vigorous. For anyone with any form of gout or arthritis, the slow, stretching movements of yoga or tai-chi will restore flexibility and break up calcium deposits in joints. Also be sure your diet contains sufficient calcium. Calcium deposits associated with arthritis are caused by an insufficiency—not a surplus—of calcium. Most people with arthritis benefit from dolomite or bone meal with vitamin D supplements.

During stage 3 of guided imagery (page 138), visualize the hordes of lymphocytes leaving the afflicted joint. Watch the swelling subside and the inflammation disappear. In stage 5, picture your joints as completely flexible and pain-free. And make a particularly strong visualization of yourself in perfect health, completely free of arthritis symptoms and pain.

Osteoarthritis is a degenerative joint disease in which the bone and cartilage wear away, causing the joints to harden and lose flexibility. Obesity is a major cause; being excessively overweight overloads the weight-bearing joints in the knees, hips, lower spine, and neck—sites where osteoarthritis most often strikes. Constant bone destruction occurs at the afflicted joints, leading to an overgrowth of new bone. New bone often grows as a spur, creating a deformity. Osteoarthritis appears most often in obese women and in overweight people aged forty and over. It is considered medically incurable.

Assuming you are overweight, visualize yourself carrying out holistic steps 2 and 3—that is, exercise plus sound nutrition. And during stage 5 of guided imagery, visualize powerful pictures of yourself entirely free of arthritis and with a spine and joints as flexible as a kitten's.

Gout is caused by eating a rich diet and becoming inactive and overweight. Alcohol, foods high in fats and oils, seafood, meat extracts and gravy, refined carbohydrates, caffeine, condiments, and spices are rich in purines, the basic substance of uric acid. When a sedentary person continually eats rich foods, an excess of uric acid spills over into the bloodstream. Uric acid crystals are deposited in the joints, causing swelling and pain.

The typical gout victim is an overweight, inactive male aged thirty to fifty. Gout usually appears as a throbbing pain in an extremity such as the big toe or in the wrist, elbow, knee, or foot. Gout can be confirmed by a blood–uric acid test made by a physician. Physicians use drugs to mask the symptoms of gout but the disease can be reversed only through holistic lifestyle changes.

Begin your imagery session by picturing yourself drinking three quarts of fluid daily in nonstimulant form (to prevent the formation of kidney stones). Then briefly visualize each of the following foods. As you do, say "No. No."

Picture a thick, black cross scrawled across the picture. The forbidden foods are anchovies, herrings, sardines, organ meats, bouillon, meat extracts, all rich meats and sausage, duck, squab, goose, all shellfish and seafood, fish roe, yeast, and alcohol. Feel repelled and nauseated by rich foods. Then picture yourself thoroughly enjoying a large, succulent vegetable salad followed by fresh fruits.

Picture yourself leaving your self-indulgent friends and meeting new, younger, athletic friends who eat natural foods and who lead a physically active, healthful lifestyle. Visualize yourself as lean and fit, leading an exciting fun life of swimming, bicycling, jogging, playing tennis, and dancing.

Once you feel these visualizations taking hold, schedule half of your stage 3 imagery for holistic steps 2 and 3, exercise plus sound nutrition. Gradually increase the imagery time allotted to holistic steps 2 and 3 until they occupy the full eight minutes of stage 3.

Inner Healing for Asthma

The basic cause of asthma is believed to be a childhood emotional disturbance that later causes the sympathetic nervous system to trigger constriction and closing of the small bronchial air passages to the lungs. Attacks are precipitated by emotional stress or by allergies.

Drugs are used to normalize the action of the autonomic nervous system but they do not cure asthma. Repeated drug use can lead to such side effects as glaucoma or peptic ulcer. Under continued drug treatment, asthma can slowly deteriorate into emphysema.

Anyone with asthma should practice progressive relaxation three times each day. Asthmatics who attain deep relaxation three times a day report a significant decline in the number of attacks. During relaxation, pay special attention to relaxing the facial muscles. Tense facial muscles cause tension to generalize throughout the head and neck, leading to constriction and congestion of the respiratory system.

Should an attack occur, begin progressive relaxation immediately. Pay special attention to relaxing the facial muscles. Prompt relaxation will frequently halt an asthma attack almost immediately.

After attaining the calm state through progressive relaxation, visualize your entire respiratory system as relaxed and wide open. See yourself breathing deeply and freely through your lungs, windpipe, and nose. Warming the hands and feet (technique #20) has also been found soothing and beneficial.

Practice technique #12 (deep breathing). Inhale deeply, drawing air down into the lower part of your lungs. Visualize yourself swimming, and picture yourself playing a wind instrument for recreation. As soon as you have the urge to do so, actually take up swimming as a regular daily exercise and begin to play a wind instrument.

While visualizing, tell yourself: "My throat feels cool. My chest feels warm."

If you still smoke, give priority to holistic step 6, stop smoking.

Inner Healing for Lower Back Pain

Most lower back pain is the result of either emotion-caused tension or lack of physical exercise. Guided imagery can help in two ways, by removing the tension and by providing the motivation to begin exercising and rehabilitating the muscularly deficient back.

Before anything else, however, you should have your back checked out by a physician or back specialist to make sure it is nothing worse than tension or muscular weakness. You should also obtain your doctor's permission to exercise. Assuming nothing more serious is involved, here is how imagery can help muscular tension and muscular weakness.

Muscular tension. Some lower back dysfunction is due to intense and sustained contraction of the lower back muscles. This tension, in turn, is due to our outdated belief system, which interprets certain life events as stressful.

Lose no time in beginning to practice progressive relaxation. Then, as you begin guided imagery, go over your entire back again, mentally relaxing every muscle. Visualize your back as heavy and warm. Picture warm, soothing blood flowing into your deeply relaxed back muscles. Visualize yourself with an athletic build, able to twist and rotate your spine in any direction and to lift heavy weights. Finally, visualize yourself rejecting all your outdated beliefs and reprogramming your mind-computer with new-beliefs. If tension is your problem, your outdated beliefs are responsible for your bad back. Picture yourself going back and studying chapters 3 through 7 of this book so that you can program emotional stress out of your life entirely.

When you've got all this going, consider doing the back-building exercises recommended below.

Muscular weakness. Lower back pain can also be caused by deficient back muscles. Dr. Hans Kraus, a well-known back specialist, found that out of three thousand of his patients who complained of back pain, 85 percent suffered from nothing more than muscularly deficient backs.

As a result of his research, Dr. Kraus has designed a back-building program that is regularly offered at YMCAs and similar institutions across the country. The courses help people retrain all the back muscles used in walk-ing, sitting, bending, and lifting to at least a minimum level of fitness. Of the first four hundred men and women to take Dr. Kraus's training, 29 percent reported a complete recovery, with full use of the back restored and all pain gone; another 36 percent reported greatly reduced pain and the ability to use the back for most purposes; and another 25 percent reported reduced pain and increased ability to undertake more activities.

Age is no barrier. When Dr. De Vries studied the effects of exercise on one hundred elderly volunteers at the Andrus Gerontology Center, he found that after a few weeks of daily exercises, most of their chronic back pain had disappeared.

Your first step is to find out where, in your area, back-building courses are available. Then use imagery to psych yourself up to take a course. Pic-ture yourself doing exercises that will rebuild your back muscles—flexing the spine, pulling knees to chest, leg raising—and see yourself enjoying them. Use technique #1 to build up the win-power you need to get started. And study chapter 7 again to learn how to create a new self-image in which flabby muscles have no part.

If no back-building course is available, consider signing up at a health spa with special consideration being given to your back. If nothing at all is avail-able, plan to begin exercising very gradually on your own. Most large book-shops and libraries carry books describing the Kraus exercises.

Use imagery to visualize yourself as perfectly fit with rippling back mus-cles and the body of an athlete. You may also want to use sunshine imagery (technique #30). For the relief of back pain alone, see technique #29, relieving chronic pain.

Inner Healing for Cardiovascular Disease

In most industrial nations, approximately half of all deaths are the result of a stroke or heart attack. These killer diseases are caused by athero-sclerosis or hardening of the arteries. A high-fat diet causes a buildup of plaques of fatty cholesterol in the arteries and smaller arterioles. The plaques reduce the lumen, or inside diameter, of the arteries, restricting the blood flow and forcing blood pressure up. When the coronary arteries—the arteries supplying the heart—become choked, the heart muscle is starved of oxygen. This creates the crushing pain of angina. Eventually, a heart attack or myocardial infarction follows.

A stroke is the result of a similar blockage in the supply of oxygen-bearing blood to the brain. A blockage in blood supply to the legs can cause claudication—an almost unbearable pain in the legs that can eventually lead to amputation.

159

Again, cardiovascular disease isn't something that just happens. We cause it ourselves through our unhealthy habits of living and eating. The causes of cardiovascular disease are a diet high in fat, salt, refined carbohydrates, and caffeine; obesity; lack of exercise; cigarette smoking; and emotional stress.

Cardiovascular disease can be prevented or reversed by practicing the seven steps to holistic health. So many studies have proved that a program of daily exercise plus a low-fat diet can reverse most risk of cardiovascular disease that cardiac rehabilitation centers have sprung up all over the country. Medically supervised records taken at the Longevity Research Center in California over a period of twenty-one months during 1976 and 1977 showed that atherosclerosis was clinically recorded in 66 percent of the nine hundred patients enrolled. Many also suffered from hypertension, diabetes, and acute heart disease. Upon beginning the standard four-week rehabilitation course, many patients were unable to walk a single block. Some had been urged to undergo bypass surgery immediately. Yet just four weeks later, the average patient was walking six miles every day.

If you have cardiovascular disease, you should enroll immediately in a cardiac rehabilitation program being offered in your area or elsewhere. If that is impossible, ask your doctor to recommend an exercise-diet program that you can follow on your own. If your doctor does not believe in non-drug cardiovascular therapy, find a doctor who does. Actually, you can plan your own program, using holistic steps 2 and 3, exercise and sound nutrition.

Your doctor's cooperation is needed only to take you off any medication and to give you permission to begin a program of very gradually increasing rhythmic exercise such as walking. If you are still smoking or drinking stimulants, read, study, and begin immediately to carry out holistic steps 5 and 6, cutting out stimulants and stopping smoking. Simultaneously, begin to practice holistic steps 2 and 3. Eliminate all fats, especially hydrogenated vegetable oils and saturated fat, from your diet along with salt and refined carbohydrates.

Use imagery to see yourself already having incorporated all these good health factors into your lifestyle. Visualize your arteries as youthful, flexible, and dilated, ballooning out with each heartbeat and completely free of cholesterol plaques. Visualize enzymes flowing through your coronary arteries, dissolving any plaques and restoring the arteries to mint condition. Visualize new, compensatory arteries appearing alongside your existing coronary arteries, bringing even more blood to the heart. Use the clock imagery in the following section to feel your heart beating with a slow, steady rhythm of sixty beats or less per minute.

Picture yourself taking long daily walks, enjoying succulent fresh fruits and vegetables, being repelled by fatty foods, and being free of the smoking and caffeine habits.

160

Repeat phrases like "I am completely free of angina pains. My angina is gone. My cardiac rehabilitation program is giving me a new lease on life. I shall outlive my life expectancy. Every day in every way I am getting better and better and better."

Meanwhile, read and study chapters 3 through 7 of this book. Eliminate all emotional stress by replacing outdated beliefs with new-beliefs. Replace all primitive expectations with rather-beliefs. Build a strong self-image, and plan goals that assume you will shortly be free of heart disease.

You should also practice technique #20 (warming the hands and feet), if possible as a preliminary step to each imagery session.

Inner Healing for Rhythmic Heart Disturbance

Fifteen percent of all deaths from heart attack are not the result of oxygen deprivation but are caused by ventricular fibrillation. Fibrillation, or heart spasm, results from a stress-related dysfunction of the heartbeat control center in the brain. It can occur in a person who is completely free of atherosclerosis or heart disease.

Tension resulting from emotional stress also overloads our neural circuits, causing such common heartbeat disorders as skipping a beat, palpitation, extra heartbeats, and irregular heart rate.

Most functional rhythmic heart disturbances arise when our mind-computer interprets a life event as stressful and becomes excited. As a result, irregular heartbeat often responds well when emotional stress is eliminated through reprogramming of the belief system. Guided imagery also has proved to be one of the most effective ways to permanently restore a calm and regular heartbeat.

The imagery for fibrillation, tachycardia, arrhythmia, or any kind of irregular heartbeat is to picture a clock with a pendulum swinging back and forth approximately sixty to seventy-two times each minute. Visualize the clock superimposed on your heart. See the pendulum steadily ticking back and forth at sixty to seventy-two ticks per minute. Hold this imagery for the full eight-minute period of stage 3.

The best suggestion is to say: "My heartbeat is steady and slow. My heartbeat is normal. Every day in every way I am getting better and better." Then count each swing of the pendulum up to sixty. Repeat the phrases. And begin counting another sixty ticks.

If you find that your natural pulse rate is faster or slower than the sixty to seventy-two range, adjust the rhythm of the clock to fit. You can ascertain your basic pulse rate by taking your pulse when sitting down at least four hours after eating or exercising. The average adult pulse rate in the United States is seventy-two beats per minute. Women have a pulse rate approximately four to six beats per minute higher than men. When you stand or move around, your pulse rate will be higher than when you are sitting down. But your basic rhythm is the one to visualize.

Do not use this visualization if you already have a pacemaker fitted. Otherwise, even if you are taking medication, imagery cannot possibly harm you. However, if you are taking medication for your heart, do not stop it without your physician's approval. Any unusual and recurring irregular heartbeat should be diagnosed by a physician.

Inner Healing for Adult-Onset Diabetes

Adult-onset diabetes is the third-highest cause of death in the United States and the average American has one chance in five of becoming diabetic at some time in life. Yet diabetes doesn't just strike out of the blue. It is the result of obesity caused by overeating a diet high in fats and refined carbohydrates, coupled with lack of exercise, smoking cigarettes, indulging in stimulants, and emotional stress. Diabetes is something we do to ourselves. Typical diabetics are Type C personalities with a self-image so poor that they bring on their own diabetes.

Poor health habits contribute to a high blood-fat level, which in turn inhibits the ability of the hormone insulin to break down sugar so that it can be burned in body cells. In most cases, it is not due to inability of the pancreas to manufacture insulin. As soon as the average adult diabetic abstains from all these wrong habits of living and eating, the diabetes disappears.

When twenty diabetics were placed on a diet-exercise program (virtually identical to our holistic health steps 2 and 3) at the Longevity Research Institute, at the end of three months their blood sugar level had dropped from a range of 150 to 350 to an average of just 96. After ninety days on the diet-exercise program, all twenty diabetics had been taken off insulin and drugs.

In another sample study at the V.A. Hospital in Lexington, Kentucky, twenty-two chronic adult diabetics were given a diet-exercise program almost identical to that of our holistic steps 2 and 3. After only three weeks, fifteen patients were able to stop all drugs and insulin. At the beginning, the twenty-two patients had an average blood sugar level of 230. But after twenty-one days of a low-fat diet, their average reading dropped to only 120. A second group of twenty diabetics on this same program achieved 100 percent reversal of diabetes.

Many diabetes specialists agree that at least three fourths of all adult-onset diabetic can be freed of dependence on drugs or insulin through exercise combined with a diet low in fat and refined carbohydrates. Supporting this view is an article in the June 1975 *Annals of Internal Medicine* by Dr. John A. Douglass of the Southern California Permanente Medicine

Group, reporting that diabetics who eat more raw vegetable foods are often able to reduce their insulin intake or to dispense with it entirely.

The role of imagery is to visualize yourself having made the necessary lifestyle changes and having completely recovered from diabetes. If you are taking medication or insulin for diabetes, you must obtain your physician's cooperation in phasing out the drugs or insulin. If your doctor is uncooperative, consider switching to a more prevention-oriented physician.

Begin by reading and putting into practice immediately holistic steps 2 and 3 as well as the remaining holistic steps to high-level wellness. If you smoke or indulge in stimulants, including caffeine, put into effect immediately holistic steps 5 and 6.

Reserve your imagery to visualize yourself at your normal weight, and visualize your pancreas producing an abundance of insulin. Place your awareness on the pancreas (located just above and behind your navel) and visualize it as a round, healthy organ about the size of a softball. See it producing a small but steady trickle of insulin.

As you do so, repeat phrases like: "My pancreas is completely healthy and produces all the insulin I need. My blood is free of fat. My weight is normal. I enjoy taking long, brisk daily walks. I enjoy eating large salads of fresh fruits and vegetables." Visualize yourself sitting down to a greasy plate of ham and eggs and feeling nauseated and repelled.

If you have any difficulty carrying out the seven holistic steps to high-level wellness, spend one imagery session daily visualizing yourself having already incorporated these steps into your lifestyle.

With your doctor's permission, you should lose no time in getting off diabetes medication or insulin. The drugs have serious side effects, and injected insulin actually damages the pancreas and its insulin-producing beta cells.

Because diabetes is worsened by stressful emotions, read chapters 3 through 7 again. Replace all outdated beliefs with new-beliefs, change all primitive expectations to rather-beliefs, and build a strong self-image with a series of goals in which you no longer have diabetes.

Note: Everything in this section applies only to adult- or maturity-onset diabetes. It does not apply to juvenile-onset diabetes.

Inner Healing for Emphysema

Usually caused by cigarette smoking, emphysema is a condition in which the alveoli, the small air sacs in the lungs, become incapable of expelling air. The disease manifests itself as a series of dry coughs, none of which can expel the mucus.

Emphysema is not completely reversible. But as a result of studies by Harry Bass, M.D., former chief of the Pulmonary Division at Peter Bent Brigham Hospital in Boston, emphysema victims are now able to learn to live comparatively normal lives. In Dr. Bass's studies, a group of male and female emphysema victims participated in daily rhythmic exercises. The patients could barely walk when the studies began, but five years later they were able to work for hours at gardening and they were even able to take moderately long walks.

Imagery is helpful in stopping smoking and in motivating the patient to want to begin exercising and recovering. If you still smoke, begin using holistic step 6, stop smoking, immediately. Once the smoking addiction is broken, visualize the exercise program in holistic step 2. Walking and swimming are the best exercises. If your emphysema is severe, check with your doctor before beginning to exercise. As you begin exercising, psych yourself up with win-power by using technique #1.

During stage 5 of guided imagery, make strong visualizations of yourself in perfect health. See yourself able to walk briskly and to swim. And plan goals that involve physical activity that is within your capabilities.

The road back from emphysema is slow and long. But as you imagine and suggest that "every day in every way I am getting better and better," so you will gradually regain use of your lungs.

Inner Healing for Hypertension (High Blood Pressure)

If allowed to go untreated over an extended period, high blood pressure can damage the arteries, heart, brain, and kidneys—increasing the risk of heart attack and stroke or damage to the kidneys and eyesight. Although it can be controlled by maintenance drugs, medical science has no cure for hypertension. The drugs have serious side effects and patient adherence to antihypertensive drugs is extremely poor. Yet it is possible to reverse hypertension through lifestyle changes and inner healing techniques.

High blood pressure is caused in one of two ways, often by both simultaneously. First, a high-fat diet, obesity, and smoking and failing to exercise cause atherosclerosis or hardening of the arteries. As cholesterol plaques increase the peripheral resistance of the arteries, the blood is squeezed and blood pressure rises. Second, whenever the mind-computer interprets a life event as stressful, the fight-or-flight state is switched on and the autonomic nervous system triggers the vasoconstrictor muscles to constrict the arteries. This compresses the blood into a smaller volume and raises the blood pressure.

However, a person's blood pressure is constantly changing. The stress of being in a doctor's office is frequently sufficient to raise blood pressure to

164

abnormal levels. This phenomenon, called lability, exists in one of every two people. Many leading heart specialists believe that millions of people who have been diagnosed as hypertensive, and who have been placed for life on antihypertensive drugs, have only labile hypertension. Their blood pressure is perfectly normal until a nurse or doctor takes it. Then it shoots up.

To eliminate this risk, get yourself a blood pressure set at a drugstore. A good-quality set costs less than two routine visits to the average doctor's office. You can learn to use the cuff and stethoscope in a single evening of practice. After that, you can take your own or anyone else's blood pressure at any time without the risk of a labile reading.

Normal blood pressure for adult Americans is 120 over 80 millimeters (120/80), meaning a systolic pressure of 120 (during contraction) and a diastolic pressure of 80 (while resting). Any reading above 140/90 is considered high. Within limits, the lower your blood pressure the better.

To lower elevated blood pressure to normal requires a holistic approach that calls for a low-fat diet, regular and abundant daily exercise, and the elimination of emotional stress. Begin by studying chapters 3 through 7. Transform all positive stress into negative stress. Replace all outdated beliefs with new-beliefs. Change all primitive expectations into rather-beliefs. Replace all negative emotions with positive emotions. Build a strong self-image. Plan goals that assume your blood pressure will be back to normal in a matter of weeks.

Next, read and put into effect the seven holistic steps to high-level wellness. Eat only a low-fat, high-fiber diet consisting primarily of fresh fruits, vegetables, and whole grains. Eliminate all saturated fats, hydrogenated vegetable oils, refined carbohydrates, and excessive animal protein. Salt is absolutely forbidden. So are smoking and drinkng caffeine and alcohol.

Begin a daily walking program. In easy, graduated stages, build up to where you are walking a minimum of six brisk miles per day.

If you have genuine hypertension, plan on three imagery sessions daily. Precede each session with technique #20 (warming the hands and feet). Read chapter 9 carefully and include the recommended tensing exercise. Hand warming and muscle tensing are essential parts of any hypertensive therapy.

During stage 3 imagery, visualize your entire nervous system as calm, limp, and relaxed. (Picture the nervous and circulatory systems like the illustrations you see in a physiology text.) Visualize the vasoconstrictor muscles that surround each artery as limp and relaxed. See your arteries as youthful and flexible, ballooning in and out with each heartbeat. See your arteries as so clear and dilated that the blood does not fill them completely.

Then visualize two tall transparent glass or plastic tubes sticking upright out of your aorta, the principal artery that carries blood from the heart.

Each tube is approximately forty-two inches tall and each is marked by a scale graduated from a reading of 200 at the top to 50 near the bottom. Picture each tube almost filled to the top with blood. The blood level pulsates with each heartbeat. One tube, which measures the systolic pressure, is filled several inches higher than the other, which shows the diastolic pressure.

Now visualize the blood slowly dropping in both tubes after each pulsation. Over a period of about one minute, see the pressure gradually drop to 115 in the systolic tube and to 75 in the diastolic tube. Keep repeating this visualization throughout the eight minutes of stage 3. You should be able to repeat the scene approximately seven times.

Meanwhile, repeat such phrases as: "I am completely calm and relaxed. I am free of emotional stress. My arteries are flexible and dilated. My arteries balloon out with each heartbeat. My blood pressure is low. My blood pressure is falling. My blood pressure is 115 over 75."

Many hypertensives are hard-driving Type A personalities. Read chapter 3 again and take firm steps to transform your lifestyle into that of a Type B personality. Use technique #1 to psych yourself up to make the changes. Reschedule your life so that you have ample time for everything. Eliminate as many time pressures and deadlines as possible. Give up some commitments if necessary. Make your life simple and uncomplicated. Stay relaxed and let go all of the time.

Because of the possibility of a tumor in the kidney or other structural change that could affect hormone production, I strongly urge anyone with elevated blood pressure to see a physician. Assuming that your doctor diagnoses your condition as essential hypertension—meaning that the cause of hypertension is unknown—you can usually count on being able to reduce it to normal by using the inner healing methods described in this book.

Depending on the individual, high blood pressure may drop back to normal within a few weeks, or it may take several months. If you are seriously overweight, you will probably not achieve normal blood pressure until you return to your normal weight.

Despite all the propaganda you hear about hypertension being incurable, this is seldom the case. It may be medically incurable, but the literature abounds with tens of thousands of cases of hypertensives who restored their blood pressure to normal by using the same therapies recommended in these pages.

Inner Healing for Benign Prostate Enlargement

Benign prostate enlargement is usually the result of years of dissipation. The sufferer is almost invariably sedentary and overweight. A urologist should be consulted to eliminate the possibility of cancer, a prostatic stone, or an infection. You should also obtain your physician's approval to begin an exercise program.

The prostate is a small, horseshoe-shaped gland that surrounds the neck of the bladder. When enlarged, it restricts the flow of urine from the bladder, causing such symptoms as frequent urination, diminution of the urinary stream, and a feeling of incomplete voiding. Benign prostate enlargement is often accompanied by prostatitis, an acute or chronic inflammation of the prostate. Any infection should be treated by a urologist.

Since prostatic enlargement is caused by unhealthy living and eating habits, it usually responds well to a complete changeover to a healthful lifestyle.

Start immediately by reading and putting into practice holistic steps 2 and 3, exercise plus sound nutrition. Also put into practice all the remaining holistic steps to high-level wellness.

Reserve the imagery sessions for technique #27 (programming your immune system to destroy infections and cancer). In this case, direct your white cells to destroy any infection in the prostate area. Also, visualize the prostate shrinking from the size of a doughnut to the size of a walnut. Visualize it as pink and healthy and free of infection. See it as causing no obstruction at all to your bladder or urinary flow. Picture your urinary stream as strong and forceful without dribbling or discomfort.

As you visualize, repeat phrases like these: "My prostate is healthy and small. My bladder is healthy and large. I sleep soundly and undisturbed all night without having to get up to urinate. I enjoy natural foods. As I follow the seven holistic steps to high-level wellness, I enjoy life more and more. Every day in every way I am getting better and better and better."

Use win-power (technique #1) to psych yourself up to make the lifestyle changes to conform to the seven holistic steps to high-level wellness. If you experience difficulty in putting any of these steps into practice, devote one imagery session daily to visualizing yourself already practicing these steps.

Once you have cut out stimulants and have built a new lifestyle around exercise and eating natural foods, you must continue these good health practices for the rest of your life. A single evening of indiscretionary drinking can make your prostate swollen again and undo the work of weeks of imagery and healthful living.

Inner Healing for Ulcers

An ulcer is a disease of stress. Production of pepsin and acid in the stomach is controlled by the hypothalamus and the autonomic nervous system. When our mind-computer interprets a life event as stressful, the hypothalamus triggers the autonomic nervous system to increase production of stomach acids. This excess acid transforms the pre-enzyme pepsinogen into the full enzyme state. The pepsin, along with acid enzymes, then attacks the mucous lining of the stomach and intestines. A sore is created, usually in the duodenum (the small intestines adjoining the stomach) or in the stomach itself.

Back in 1950, ulcers were twenty times more common in males than in females. But as women have entered more stressful occupations, the ratio is now only two to one. Most stomach ulcers occur before age fifty—the high-stress years. Whenever stress occurs, ulcer pain increases and the ulcer may bleed. Food and milk relieve pain while acid-producing caffeine, alcohol, aspirin, or smoking intensify pain.

If your negative emotions can eat a hole in your stomach, your positive emotions can heal it. Healing with the mind is the best, fastest, and most certain way to reverse an ulcer.

The first and most immediate step is to transform all positive stress into negative stress. Begin by studying chapters 3 through 7. Replace all outdated beliefs with new-beliefs. Change all primitive expectations into rather-beliefs. Replace all negative emotions with positive emotions. Build a strong self-image. Plan goals that assume you will be free of your ulcer in a matter of weeks.

Whenever you feel emotional stress about to occur, immediately use the sudden-stop method (technique #2).

Next, read, study, and practice the seven holistic steps to high-level wellness. Have your doctor take you off all medications, like aspirin or steroids, that irritate ulcers.

Reserve your imagery for visualizing your ulcer healing. During stage 1, picture your ulcer as a round, red sore in the duodenum or stomach. An excess of acids and enzymes triggered by stress causes a raw, empty feeling that soon becomes a sharp pain.

In stage 2, visualize any antacid or other ulcer medication coating the ulcer with a soothing sheath that neutralizes the corroding enzymes. As the pain is soothed, flow on without interruption into stage 3 imagery.

Visualize healthy, new pink tissue growing over the sore and causing the ulcer to disappear. Repeat this for eight full minutes. Then flow into stage 4 and see your stomach lining completely free and clear of any sore. In stage 5, see yourself free of all emotional stress and in a permanent state of calm and peace. Flow into stage 6 and picture yourself achieving a goal that might be difficult to attain with an ulcer.

Accompany the imagery with such phrases as: "I always feel calm and at peace. My ulcer pain is gone. My ulcer has healed over. Every day in every way I feel better and better and better."

Inner Healing for Ulcerative Colitis

Ulcerative colitis is a chronic inflammation and swelling of the mucous lining of the colon. The colon is easily damaged and often bleeds. Dehydration and diarrhea are among the many uncomfortable symptoms. The cause is believed to involve the immune system's inability to produce sufficient antibodies to counteract the excessive antigens in the colon. Thus this autoimmune disease leads to loss of colon function with constant risk of cancer or severe infection. It strikes most often between the ages of twenty and forty during periods of high stress.

Medical treatment ranges from massive doses of antibiotics and cortisone to a colostomy (surgical removal of the colon), which turns the patient into a lifelong invalid.

However, the many small Nature Cure healing centers around the country report a very satisfying rate of permanent reversal of ulcerative colitis without drugs or surgery. These healing centers teach the patient to make permanent lifestyle changes based on the same principles as the seven holistic steps to high-level wellness. Some also use an extended water fast. But the most important therapeutic factor always seems to be elimination of emotional stress.

As a first and vital step, review chapters 3 through 7. Replace all outdated beliefs with new-beliefs. Transform all primitive expectations into rather-beliefs. Replace all negative emotions with positive emotions. Turn all positive stress into negative stress. Build a strong self-image. And plan goals that assume you will be free of ulcerative colitis in a few months.

Then use imagery to see your colon free of inflammation and completely well. Visualize yourself restored to perfect health, able to run and lead an active life free of diarrhea, hemorrhoids, and all the other discomforts of the disease. You can also use imagery to motivate yourself to adopt each of the seven holistic steps to high-level wellness. Psych yourself up with frequent bouts of win-power (technique #1).

After eliminating stress, the seven holistic steps to high-level wellness are the therapy for ulcerative colitis. Build these good health habits into your lifestyle and retain them permanently. As you remove the cause of the disease, your own body's recuperative powers will restore a state of optimum wellness.

Bibliography

Index

Bibliography

Anderson, R. *Stress Power.* New York: Human Sciences Press, 1978.

Assagioli, R. *The Act of Will.* New York: Viking Press, 1973.

Barber, T., and Stoyva, J. *Biofeedback and Self-control.* Chicago: Aldine-Atherton, 1972.

Bathrop, R. "Depressed Lymphocyte Function after Bereavement." *Lancet,* 16 April 1977.

Benet, S. *How to Live to Be 100: The Lifestyle of the People of the Caucasus.* New York: Dial Press, 1976.

Benson, H. *The Relaxation Response.* New York: William Morrow, 1975.

Berne, E. *Games People Play.* New York: Grove Press, 1964.

Brown, B. *New Mind, New Body.* New York: Harper and Row, 1975.

Brown, B. *Supermind: The Ultimate Energy.* New York: Harper and Row, 1980.

Coopersmith, S. *The Antecedents of Self-esteem.* San Francisco: W. H. Freeman and Company, 1967.

Davies, D. *The Centenarians of the Andes.* Garden City, New York: Anchor Press/Doubleday, 1975.

Dyer, W. *Your Erroneous Zones.* New York: Funk and Wagnalls, 1976.

Ellis, A., and **Harper, R.** *A Guide to Rational Living.* North Hollywood, Calif.: Wilshire Book Company, 1973.

Ford, N. *Good Health without Drugs.* New York: St. Martin's Press, 1978.

_____. *Secrets of Staying Young and Living Longer.* Floral Park, New York: Harian Press, 1979.

_____. *Natural Ways to Relieve Pain.* Floral Park, New York: Harian Press, 1980.

Friedman, M., and **Rosenman, R.** *Type-A Behavior and Your Heart.* New York: Alfred A. Knopf, 1974.

Green, E. and **Green, A.** *Beyond Biofeedback.* New York: Delacorte Press, 1977.

Green, E., Green, A.; Ferguson, D.; **Walters, E.** *Preliminary Report on Voluntary Controls Project: Swami Rama.* Topeka, Kans.: Menninger Foundation, 1970.

Harris, T. *I'm O.K. You're O.K.* New York: Harper and Row, 1967.

Hrachovec, J. *Keeping Young and Living Longer.* Los Angeles: Sherbourne Press, 1972.

Hutschnecker, A. *The Will to Live.* New York: Thomas A. Crowell, 1953.

Isherwood C., and **Swami Prabhavananda.** *How to Know God: The Yoga Aphorisms of Patanjali.* Hollywood, Calif.: Vedanta Press, 1953.

James, M., and **Jongeward, D.** *Born to Win.* Menlo Park, Calif.: Addison-Wesley, 1971.

Jung, C. G. *Man and His Symbols.* New York: Doubleday, 1964.

Kamiya, J.; Tart, C.; et al. *Altered States of Consciousness.* New York: John Wesley and Sons, 1969.

Karlins, M., and **Andrews, L.** *Biofeedback: Turning on the Power of Your Mind.* Philadelphia: J. B. Lippincott, 1972.

Keyes, K. *Handbook to Higher Consciousness.* St. Mary's, Ky.: Living Love Institute, 1975.

La Motte, K. *Escape from Stress.* New York: Berkeley Publishing, 1975.

Lawrence, J. *Alpha Brain Waves.* New York: Nash Publishing, 1972.

Le Shan, L. *You Can Fight for Your Life.* New York: M. Evans and Company, 1977.

Lewis, H., and **Lewis, M.** *Psychosomatics: How Your Emotions Can Damage Your Health.* New York: Viking Press, 1972.

Loomis, E., and **Paulson, J.** *Healing for Everyone: Medicine of the Whole Person.* New York: Hawthorne Books, 1975.

Lowen, A. *Depression and the Body: The Biological Basis of Faith and Reality.* New York: Coward, McCann and Geoghegan, 1972.

Luria, A. *The Working Brain.* New York: Basic Books, 1973.

Luthe, W. *Autogenic Therapy.* Vols. 1–5. New York: Grune and Stratton, 1969.

Kushel, G. *Centering: Six Steps towards Inner Liberation.* New York: Times Books, 1979.

Maharishi Mahesh Yogi. *The Science of Being and the Art of Living.* London: International SRM Publications, 1966.

Maltz, M. *Psychocybernetics.* New York: Pocket Books, 1966.

Maslow, A. *The Farther Reaches of Human Nature.* New York: Viking Press, 1971.

Missildine, H. *Your Inner Child of the Past.* New York: Simon and Schuster, 1963.

Naranjo, C., and **Ornstein, R.** *On the Psychology of Meditation.* New York: Viking Press, 1971.

Ornstein, R. *The Psychology of Consciousness.* San Francisco: W. H. Freeman, 1972.

Pelletier, K. *Mind as Healer, Mind as Slayer.* New York: Delta Press, 1977.

Pelletier, K., and **Garfield, C.** *Consciousness East and West.* New York: Harper and Row, 1976.

Perls, F.; Hefferline, R.; Goodman, P. *Gestalt Therapy.* New York: Dell Publishing, 1951.

Pritikin, 9N.; Leonard, J.; Hofer, L. *Live Longer Now.* New York: Grosset and Dunlap, 1974.

Rhinehart, L. *The Book of Est.* New York: Holt, Rhinehart and Winston, 1976.

Richardson, A. *Mental Imagery.* New York: Springer Publishing, 1969.

Rosenfeld, E. *The Book of Highs.* New York: Times Books, 1973.

Samuels, M., and **Bennett, H.** *The Well Body Book.* New York: Random House, 1973.

174

Samuels, M., and Samuels, N. *Seeing with the Mind's Eye.* New York: Random House, 1975.

Schultz, H., and Luthe, W. *Autogenic Training: A Psychophysical Approach in Psychotherapy.* New York: Grune and Stratton, 1959.

Seligman, M. *Helplessness: On Depression, Development and Death.* San Francisco: W. H. Freeman, 1975.

Selye, H. *Stress without Distress.* Philadelphia: J. B. Lippincott, 1974.

Selye, H. *The Stress of Life.* New York: McGraw-Hill, 1956.

Shealy, N. *The Pain Game.* Millbrae, Calif.: Celestial Arts Press, 1976.

Shealy, N. *Ninety Days to Self-Health.* New York: Dial Press, 1977.

Shelton, H. *Natural Hygiene: Man's Pristine Way of Life.* Chicago: Natural Hygiene Press, 1968.

Silva J., and Miele, P. *The Silva Mind Control Method.* New York: Simon and Schuster, 1977.

Simonton, C.; Simonton, S.; Achterberg, J. *Stress, Psychological Factors, and Cancer.* Fort Worth, Tex.: New Medicine Press, 1976.

Simonton, C.; Simonton, S.; Creighton, J. *Getting Well Again.* Los Angeles: J. P. Tarcher, 1978.

Stevens, J. *Awareness: Exploring, Experimenting, Experiencing.* New York: Real People Press, 1971.

Swami Satchidananda. *Integral Yoga Hatha.* New York: Holt, Rhinehart and Winston, 1970.

Swami Vishnudevananda. *The Complete Illustrated Book of Yoga.* New York: Julian Press, 1960.

Trop, J. *You Don't Have to Be Sick.* Chicago: Natural Hygiene Press, 1961.

Wilson, D. *Total Mind Power.* New York: Berkeley Publishing, 1978.

Index